One Man's Full Life

Earl E. Bakken

Medtronic, Inc.

Published by Medtronic, Inc.
7000 Central Avenue NE
Minneapolis, MN 55432

Cover and book design by Patrick Delmore

Printed in the United States of America

Library of Congress Catalog Card Number 99-60645

ISBN 0-9670619-0-3

To Doris, my wife
and best friend; to my children;
to Doris's children; and to
our grandchildren – all of whom
I love with a full and
grateful heart.

Contents

Acknowledgements

Though this book is an autobiography, the efforts of several associates, friends, and loved ones have been necessary to shepherd it into print.

Those helpful persons include my wife, Doris Bakken, and my sister, Marjorie Anderson, who read the manuscript at various stages and made valuable suggestions; at Medtronic, director and former president Tom Holloran, director of employee and financial communications Carla Bender, director of media relations Dick Reid, and communications manager Carol Riach, all of whom reviewed the manuscript and did their best to make sure my memory for historical detail was up to the job, and creative services director Pat Delmore, who was responsible for the book's handsome design and oversaw its production; and at The Bakken Library & Museum, executive director David Rhees. Special thanks goes to Bill George, Medtronic's chairman and CEO, for his generous Foreword, and to Susan Pueschel at the North Hawaii Community Hospital for her kind Afterword.

I am especially indebted to my long-time associate and right-hand man, Ron Hagenson; my indispensable administrative assistant at Medtronic, Karen Larson; my resourceful personal secretary in Kiholo Bay, Laurieanne Atwood; and Medtronic's former vice president for communications, Celia Barnes, for their roles in defining the project and guiding it to publication. William Swanson, a Minneapolis-based writer and editor, helped me plumb a lifetime's experience and find the right words to recount it.

Thank you all. This book wouldn't exist without your suggestions, encouragement, and hard work.

– Earl E. Bakken

Foreword

By *William W. George*
Chairman and Chief Executive Officer, Medtronic, Inc.

Only rarely in life do you have the opportunity to work closely with a true pioneer, a person who, through his vision, inspiration, courage, and leadership, can change the course of human history.

Earl Bakken is such a person.

He not only invented the world's first wearable, battery-operated external pacemaker, he helped launch the modern medical-technology industry. Through his leadership, he enabled millions of people with life-threatening illnesses to be restored to full life and health. He founded and led the world's leading medical-technology company. And now, in his eighth decade, he is pioneering again, creating an entirely new form of healing.

As is evident throughout this autobiography, Earl Bakken is a visionary: a man who can dream of a future unthinkable to others and then lead people to enable his dream to become a reality. Earl's dreams are often so advanced that others scoff at them, or simply ignore him. They do so at their peril, for Earl has spent a lifetime making his dreams come true.

He is a man of paradox: an engineer who envisions a world of "high-touch" integrated healing, a leader who inspires others, but lets them do their own thing, an introvert who will happily stand on a convention floor for 12 hours at a time, talking to prospective users of his ideas.

My first meeting with Earl was unusual, to say the least, and it says a lot about his character and commitment. It happened in early 1989, when I was working for Honeywell and visiting one of our divisions in Phoenix, Arizona. Believe it or not, Earl flew from Kona, Hawaii, to meet me at the Marriott Courtyard Inn in Phoenix to persuade me to join Medtronic as president and chief operating officer.

Our dinner together was certainly not a typical job interview. Earl asked me no questions about my business background, leadership abilities, or management style. Instead, he spent most of the evening talking about chaos (in the mathematical sense), chronobiology, and advances in treating neurological diseases for which there had never been any cures! His thoughts were way over my head, but I did my best to keep the conversation going.

Three days later I received a letter from Earl saying, "I have looked for many years for a person to lead our company for the next generation. I believe you are that person." Needless to say, that vote of confidence and Earl's unusual "recruiting visit" had a big impact on my decision to join Medtronic.

Earl has been doing things like that all his life. He seeks out the people with whom he would like to work and attracts them to his cause through his vision and his inspiration. He started with a small company in a garage in northeast Minneapolis 50 years ago and hasn't let up for a moment since.

On paper Earl retired from Medtronic in 1989, but in fact he is hardly retired! Almost 10 years later he is busier than ever, creating the world's first "integrated healing center" in Waimea, Hawaii, and turning the Big Island of Hawaii into a "Healing Island."

What are the qualities that have allowed Earl Bakken to accomplish so much in his lifetime? He has deep technical knowledge, but so do many other engineers who never reach beyond the confines of their laboratories. He has vision, but so do many others whose ideas never come to fruition. He has leadership skill, but the world is filled with leaders who never go beyond a single major accomplishment.

What makes Earl unique, in my opinion, is his soul. Earl is a man with a mission to use science to benefit humankind, an idea he received from his pastor in his early teenage years and from which he has never deviated. He has a deep sense of spiritual calling, an understanding of his purpose on this earth.

And, more than any person I have ever met, Earl is totally devoted to his calling. Nothing can cause him to deviate or to give up. Money, fame, glory...Earl has all of these, but none is really important to him. He conveys his mission to everyone he meets, and he openly, yet modestly, asks them to join him on his journey.

His sense of spirituality is most evident in his legacy and the symbols of that legacy. For example, at Medtronic he initiated a holiday program in 1959, an event that captures the real meaning of Medtronic and of Earl Bakken. Each December six patients, their families, and their physicians journey to Minneapolis to tell several thousand Medtronic employees how their lives were restored by Medtronic products. There are many tears, but through it all shines the purpose of their work for every person in that room. Earl's modest role is to preside at the event and to introduce the patients. No great speeches – instead Earl lets the patient stories speak for themselves.

In 1960, with his fledgling company facing bankruptcy resulting from too much success with the pacemaker and too little capital to build the business, Earl sat down and wrote Medtronic's now-famous mission statement. Not a word of that statement has changed in 38 years, and Earl talks about the company's mission with the same passion he did when it was new.

That mission enabled Earl to raise the venture-capital funds he needed to keep going. And today the once nearly bankrupt company is valued by its public investors at more than $27 billion!

Since drafting Medtronic's mission statement, Earl has met personally with almost every new employee, to describe the founding of the company, its mission, and its values. Toward the end of the two-hour meeting, Earl asks each new employee to come forward and receive a bronze medallion that illustrates the mission with the Medtronic symbol of the "Rising Man" and the words "Toward Full Life" engraved on it.

In giving them the medallion, Earl asks the employees to make their own commitment to fulfilling the mission with the words, "You are here not to make money for yourself or the company, but to restore people to full life." Pretty powerful words for, say, a newly immigrated Asian-American production employee – or a new chief operating officer!

Medtronic's mission statement calls for the company "to be recognized as a company of dedication, honesty, integrity, and service." Throughout his life Earl Bakken has made these values his touchstone and has always emulated the highest standards of these values in his daily life.

As you read this autobiography, I hope you will be as inspired as I've been by Earl's life, work, and the vision he has made reality.

Bill George

Introduction

One Man's Full Life

The thought of publishing your own life story takes some getting used to, especially if you're not a big-time politician, athlete, or entertainer, or otherwise engaged in a field where talking about yourself in public is an everyday part of the job. I'm not sure I'm entirely comfortable with the idea yet, though, truth be told, this book has been under consideration and given intermittent attention since 1992.

At one time in my life the prospect of talking at length and in detail about myself and my activities would, indeed, have been unthinkable. You will understand why, I trust, when you read about my conservative, middle-class, Minnesota Lutheran upbringing and my early vision of a rich and fulfilled life centered on an obscure corner of a research laboratory where I could practice the engineer's trade in anonymity. That there is such a book at all testifies to what came later – also described in the following pages – which was, first, my deliberate transformation from an introverted entrepreneur to a slightly less introverted corporate leader and, second, the once-unimaginable success of Medtronic, Inc., the $4.0-billion company I helped found, and the opportunities afforded me by that success.

Success in most any field, I assume, will give a person some confidence. Success in the field of medical technology gave me, in addition, whole new worlds of opportunity and ideas. It allowed me to work with and learn from some of the great minds of contemporary science and medicine. It allowed me to travel to all parts of the globe, finally leading me to a place that may be as close to paradise as I could ever expect to find while still on earth. Most important, it allowed me to explore and eventually put in practice many of the concepts involving health and healing that have, in one form or another, preoccupied my conscious and subconscious minds almost my entire life. I am indeed a fortunate person, not only for that success, but for those particular rewards.

Even so, my original intentions for this book were modest. I would simply produce a little memoir for my children and grandchildren. I had officially retired from my formal duties at Medtronic and reached the age when men and women think seriously about their mortality. Heaven knows there had been, by that time, a considerable amount of information written, recorded, and even filmed about the company, its history, industry, and products (especially the cardiac pacemaker). There was even a surprising number of press clippings, monographs, speeches, and other materials prepared about, for, or by me. My original aim was to condense some of that material, synthesize it with my current thoughts and activities, and publish the result in a single, accessible, easy-to-digest package. That is, between the covers of a book.

Then I began thinking that perhaps there might be some interest in my experience and ideas among a broader audience than just my family. Encouraged by Medtronic, I had been speaking for some time to a wide range of industry and professional organizations, civic associations, academic assemblies, and student groups both in the United States and abroad; now I wondered whether members of those groups might be interested in my book. In 1990 I published a series of brief "leadership essays" that covered some of the essential lessons I had learned starting and running a company, and, much to my surprise, those essays, though intended for Medtronic's internal consumption, were widely read and commented upon. Maybe the readers of the essays would be interested in what Paul Harvey would call "the rest of the story."

Some of my friends and colleagues suggested that readers beyond my immediate personal and corporate families might be curious about the apparently contradictory streams of high technology and "low-tech" healing coming together in one man's career. Why, they might wonder, was this electrical engineer and businessman from the Snow Belt now promoting acupuncture, hands-on healing, and other holistic therapies in sunny Hawaii? Why was a pioneer of cardiac pacing and other sophisticated electronic medical devices now insisting that technology is only part of the answer to restoring patients to full life and that what is most important is our ability to turn on the "healer within"? I knew from my own interaction with a lot of different people over the past several years that there was interest in such questions, and that not the least of that interest would be found in the worldwide medical community where I had spent my working life.

I eventually decided, then, to direct my story to a considerably wider group of readers than my kids and grandkids. Ideally, I'd reach members of the health-care, healing, and technology communities (wherever they might be located), health-care policymakers in both private and public sectors, educators and business leaders in non-health and non-technology fields, and persons in and outside of health and technology fields who dream of or have already been involved in starting their own businesses. I became especially intrigued by the idea of speaking to young people – high school and college students – and sharing with them some of the excitement and possibilities awaiting their entry into science, medicine, and related areas of endeavor.

Given the breadth of the audience I've come to envision for this book, I've tried to speak in the plainest possible language, avoiding narrow technical terms and descriptions. Indeed, in keeping with my emphasis on the "high-touch" approach to health care, this book is more about people than technology, though, as I said earlier, the success of our devices has made so much of the rest of the story possible. Similarly, this book is only partly about Medtronic, though Medtronic, as developer of those devices, has been the engine for so much more. I'm afraid, nonetheless, that there are many, many people who could and should find an honored place in this story, but are mentioned only briefly (or not at all), on account of time and space limitations or lapses of my memory. I wish I could acknowledge you all, but I can't, so I won't make matters worse by pretending.

I can't emphasize enough, though, that this is far more than just one man's life story. It is the story of many lives – including those of my mother and father, my teachers and mentors, my colleagues and collaborators, my friends and neighbors, and, of course, my wonderful family – all of whom have, in one significant way or another, intersected, influenced, and enriched my own. Little of what I've accomplished – little of what I think and do –

would have been possible without all of those lives and countless others over the years. I'm profoundly grateful to each and all.

There are, besides those lives, some themes I believe are especially important to the following story.

One is the concept of *Ready, fire, aim*. Perhaps only when you've trekked deep into your eighth decade do you really appreciate how fast time passes and how little time we have to accomplish our goals. We in the scientific and technological communities especially, I think, tend to study things to death, to demand too much "proof" of a phenomenon's efficacy, to worry too much about statistical significance – while, in the meantime, patients suffer and business opportunities flash past. Excessive regulation and the constant threat of litigation, especially in the United States, have contributed greatly to our over-cautiousness, but too often we're constrained by our own timidity in the face of risk and an almost paralyzing fear of failure. As I try to make plain in the narrative that follows, most of the good things in my life and career have come to pass because somebody was willing to rush in where more careful folks were afraid to tread.

Another theme is the need to treat technology and the human touch as complementary forces. I've devoted most of my life to the development of leading-edge electronic devices, but I've learned that technology is most effective – in many cases is effective only – when combined with the awesome power of the human mind, spirit, and hand. This belief, based on years of personal observation as well as scientific study, does not in any way detract from our spectacular technological achievements; on the contrary, it reinforces, enhances, and perpetuates the devices' remarkable effectiveness. The interconnectedness of all matter and phenomena should, by this time in our human experience, not only be acknowledged but incorporated and even celebrated in our lives and work.

Finally, I hope to make it clear that at the heart of all my increasingly disparate activities has been a genuine desire to help people lead better lives. That desire is the legacy of my parents, especially my loving mother, Florence (who passed away, at the age of 94, in 1995), and the shared interest of my late brother-in-law, Palmer Hermundslie, with whom I co-founded Medtronic in 1949, and the ongoing commitment of that company's 20,000-plus employees around the world and the driving force of the "Healing

Island" my friends and I are striving to establish in Hawaii. For all of us, and for our thousands of colleagues in the healing arts and sciences, the concept of restoring men and women to full, productive lives has been more than a corporate stratagem; it's been a way of life. I am honored and privileged to have been – to be – a small part of that noble effort.

This story begins with my life today in Hawaii – with, more precisely, the miraculous birth of "a new kind of hospital" and our hopes and dreams for a healing community on the Big Island. Then it goes backward in time to my boyhood home in Minneapolis, my introduction to both life and electricity, my education at the University of Minnesota, and the decidedly inauspicious formation of Medtronic shortly after World War II. I describe the small, shaky efforts of the company through its first decade, the creation of the world's first battery-powered, wearable cardiac pacemaker, and the uncertain beginnings of the implantable medical device industry. I share the tremendous (and unexpected) boom of that industry and the tremendous (and unexpected) contributions (and occasional tribulations) of Medtronic, and some of the lessons learned in the process. Finally, at story's end, I come back, full circle, to Hawaii, where I find all the contentment and challenge that a "retired" entrepreneur can reasonably be expected to handle.

From my perspective, it's been an incredible journey. Now that I've cranked up the nerve to share it, I trust that you'll find it an interesting and maybe even enlightening trip.

ONE

A Healing Island

On April 20, 1996, I witnessed a miracle.

In the shadow of mighty Mauna Kea, the highest point on the Hawaiian islands and the largest volcanic mountain in the world, a small, rural hospital was dedicated. Now ordinarily a hospital dedication wouldn't attract much attention, let alone be described as miraculous. But this wasn't an ordinary hospital. As if to provide testimony to its extraordinariness, not one, not two, but 15 different religious faiths were invoked during the ceremony. Clearly, the North Hawaii Community Hospital, in little Waimea, on the Big Island of Hawaii, was a very special – a very spiritual – place.

As it happened, the opening of the NHCH wasn't the first miracle I've been privileged to witness in my lifetime. Almost 40 years earlier I watched a small electrical device – cobbled together with spare parts according to a diagram for an electronic metronome borrowed from a popular magazine – keep an infant heart patient alive. Several years after that, I proudly watched the company I helped found back in 1949 and presided over during decades of struggle and crisis leap past the billion-dollar sales mark as the world's leading manufacturer of implantable medical technology. That the company, Medtronic, had survived its first year was a miracle in its own right.

Sometimes, indeed, I have to pinch myself to make sure the entire miraculous journey from a snowy neighborhood in northeast Minneapolis to this verdant slice of paradise in northwest Hawaii hasn't been a dream. In a sense, of course, it has. But then I consider myself a visionary and a futurist. I believe in dreams and visions. Dreams and visions have a way, I've learned, of predicting and preceding reality.

. . .

The North Hawaii Community Hospital was not my dream, at least not until recently. It was, however, the dream of many residents of the Big Island's northwest corner going back to the 1930s. My wife Doris and I discovered, upon our settling here more than seven years ago, that in fact a handful of concerned citizens had been actively working toward such a facility years earlier. It had been a valiant but unsuccessful struggle. Hospitals are big, complex, and expensive projects, and without a lot of money and clout they often don't get built, regardless of the community's need and the hard work of their advocates. The Big Island was the poorest of the Hawaiian islands. The population of mostly rural, sparsely settled north Hawaii was in poor health even by Big Island standards, the 29,000 residents lacking an up-to-date and appropriately equipped medical facility and information. But while there was demonstrable need, there were neither the funds nor the political muscle to make that particular dream come true. Then, slowly, incrementally, the process began to redevelop. In 1986, Dr. Sharon Vitousek, a physician practicing in the town of Waimea, lost a young patient to injuries suffered in an auto accident because there wasn't a medical center close enough to permit timely treatment. (Most north Hawaiians traveled either to Kona or Hilo for their medical care, driving, in some cases, an hour-and-a-half, one way, for help.) There and then she decided she was going to get such a center built in the northwest corner. With the help of an emergency medical technician named Susan Pueschel, who was then working at the Lucy Henriques Clinic nearby, Dr. Vitousek began rallying the community and searching for ways to pay for the venture.

I was intrigued when I learned about the group's efforts not long after Doris and I had settled down on nearby Kiholo Bay. (Dr. Vitousek's husband, Randy, a lawyer, happened to be doing some legal work for me at the time. When he told his wife that I was on a hospital board back in Minneapolis, she wasted no time in contacting me.) But I was retired, with a flock of diverse interests to pursue in my newly claimed "leisure." I was, after years of building and running a company, pleased to spend some time simply walking the beach and relaxing in my hammock. So when they asked me to serve on their board, I said no. I said I'd be willing to attend a meeting a couple of times a year, but that would be the extent of it. Famous last words. Sharon was very persistent, and I finally agreed to serve in an advisory role. Within a short time I was hooked. The better acquainted I became with these wonderful people and the more I understood the community's need for a hospital, the more I felt compelled to pitch in and help. Before I knew it, I was deeply absorbed in the project. I'd eventually, in fact, be elected president of the new hospital's board.

Truth be told, it wasn't only the community's need and the dedication of my new neighbors that drew me in. It was the opportunity to explore some of the ideas involving holistic medicine I had acquired over the past several years. It was the once-in-a-lifetime chance to help build – from the ground up – a state-of-the-art health-care facility designed around and for the patient, not the health-care professional, and that incorporated, for the patient's sake, the best of all kinds of medicine, allopathic and "alternative" alike. Here, I came to realize, I could once more be involved in something new and important and large enough to revolutionize the treatment of suffering human beings. Our primary concern would be the health and well-being of the people of north Hawaii, but what we accomplished here could change the way health care is perceived and provided the world over.

Eventually I wrote a paper entitled, "Not Just Another Hospital," in which (prior to the actual groundbreaking) I laid out my personal vision for the new North Hawaii Community Hospital. I pointed out that while my life's work had been in the field of medical technology, and that while I strongly believed in and supported the use of the latest technology in medical treatment, there is a human side to healing that must be (but too often is not) considered. I expressed, moreover, my concern about what seemed to me to be a declining level of health-care quality even as the cost of that care seemed to be perpetually rising. Given that background and having such concerns, what, I asked, should the new hospital I was helping to build be all about? There were, in fact, a number of ways the NHCH could and should be different.

First of all, the new hospital would be patient-centered. It would not be a "machine shop" where human bodies, like mechanical equipment, are taken to be repaired. (As a businessman, I had learned from experience the vital importance of putting the customer front and center; in a hospital setting, that customer is, of course, the patient.) The patient might like to have, for example, a scenic view out his or her window, a pleasantly furnished room with a door opening directly on the grounds, savory as well as nutritious meals, liberal visiting hours, ready access to his or her medical records, and a congenial, open, and understanding relationship with the entire staff, from the doctors to the housekeepers. Above all, this hospital would be a healing instrument, providing a total healing environment.

I also hoped, I said, that the new hospital would practice what many of us call "integrated" or "complementary" medicine (both of which terms I prefer to "alternative"). In other words, the facility's medical staff would be open to a variety of healers and healing techniques that might not have been part of the conventional Western medical-school curriculum, and that whatever methods and techniques are employed would serve to "turn on the natural healer within the patient." There is, after all, only one effective healing mechanism in the world, and that is the healing capability we have built into our bodies. It is a marvelous capability, but it has to be turned on and not suppressed. What we call integrated or complementary medicine refers to treatment methods that may not be amenable to double-blind studies and conventional statistical measurements, but do produce positive, long-term outcomes from the patient's point of view. We've done great harm, I'm afraid, by requiring medical care to conform to such statistical standards. What counts – or should count – is the long-term level of quality of life the treatment provides. Complementary medicine has a positive long-term effect on the quality of the patient's life – often referred to in medical circles as the Health Related Quality of Life, or HRQL.

I believed, further, that the new hospital should play a major role in teaching harmony in people's lives. Part of that harmony derives from the state of health of the physical body – that largely mechanical, chemical, electrical entity in which we live – but the other, equally essential components are the mind and the spirit. The stimuli that affect mind and spirit – be they pleasant sensory input, caring human relationships, religious faith, or whatever – affect the body as well. Thus I felt a major function of the hospital should be educating the community on the importance of harmony to the health of mind, spirit, and body.

· · ·

About the same time as I wrote that paper, the board of directors of a group called the Archaeus Project described their thoughts on the "cyberphysiologic hospital" – a new kind of healing center that would acknowledge and incorporate an understanding of the relationship between the patient's mind, body, and spirit in the healing process. That group – which I had started back in Minneapolis, was now based in Hawaii, and included medical professionals, care providers, and other interested people – recommended dozens of components for a new kind of hospital, many of those components based on the experience of the Planetree Model Hospital Project at Pacific Presbyterian Hospital in San Francisco and other innovative care experiments around the world.

The group's recommendations for the new hospital environment included, for example:

Windows offering a salubrious outside view, with the patient's bed positioned so he or she can easily take advantage of the vista. The windows, for that matter, can be opened (though also locked and controlled if necessary); sliding doors, in every room, can give the patient direct access to fresh air, gardens, and the grounds.

The use of skylights to bring natural light into rooms and hallways.

The provision of cots, hide-a-beds, and other convertible furniture to accommodate family members who may wish to spend a night in the patient's room. A well-equipped kitchen would be available nearby so the patient's loved ones can cook, when feasible, their own food for the patient and themselves. Recorded music, as well as instruments like the piano and ukelele, would be used to create (or allow the patients and their families to create) a soothing and healing environment.

Rheostats on lighting fixtures would allow customized illumination within patient and guest areas, and only state-of-the-art fluorescent lighting would be used. Similarly, individual room temperature controls would give patients and their families individualized comfort.

Pleasing lively colors – instead of the drab institutional greens and tans common to most hospitals – would be used throughout the facility, and a rotating collection of artwork for the walls would allow patients to choose for their own rooms the scenes and subjects they find soothing.

For the new treatment techniques, the Archaeus Project board described the growing recognition granted by some hospitals to chiropractors, acupuncturists, massage and music therapists, and naturopaths, and urged an open-minded approach to complementary therapies. Certain populations, the board noted, place great faith in herbal medicine, acupuncture, healing music, homeopathy, and Hawaiian La'au lapa'au practices. Almost any therapy will have at least a cyberphysiological effect, since it is a form of attention to the patient and may make him or her more comfortable with technological medicine and the hospital environment.

As for staffing and operations, suggestions included:

Highly automated, state-of-the-art computerized record-keeping. The objective would be to make patient records immediately accessible to the patients themselves and to streamline – and thereby reduce the associated bureaucratic costs of – administrative paperwork.

The use of primary nursing, where one nurse is assigned to most functions for a group of patients, rather than separate nurses providing separate functions such as monitoring blood pressure and taking blood samples. Patients are more comfortable dealing with fewer nurses, with whom they have a better chance to develop trusting relationships. The primary nurse would also be responsible for staying in touch with the patient for a specified period following the patient's discharge from the hospital.

Maximum availability of fresh foods, with attention paid to cultural preferences. The patient and his or her care partner should be educated in diet and nutrition as part of the hospital experience.

No restrictions on visiting hours or on the visits of children, except as imposed by the patient and his or her primary-care nurse.

The actual North Hawaii Community Hospital that opened in the spring of 1996 could not incorporate every one of those goals and recommendations, but the reality, I'm pleased to say, was gratifyingly close to the community's vision and does in fact offer a "working laboratory" where many of the techniques that could be the hallmark of 21st-century health care can be evaluated.

Our new NHCH is a remarkable place indeed. When, during the first few days of operation, I told the curious media from all over the islands that "there is nothing like this in the world," I wasn't exaggerating. Nowhere else has the most advanced diagnostic and therapeutic technology (including the latest CAT scanner – best in the state) been integrated with millennia-old healing techniques the way it has here; and nowhere else has the merging of "high-tech" and "high-touch" been so deliberate and systematic. For the 29,000 north Hawaiians it serves, the private, nonprofit facility will provide emergency care, child delivery, and other vital healing services close to home and, to many of our eyes, in the most beautiful natural setting in the world.

Not surprisingly, the north Hawaii community is pleased to have the new hospital in its backyard. Nor is it unexpected that hospital planners and health-care administrators from all over the world are flying in to take a good, close look at this "hospital of the future." What these officials are seeing first-hand is a 79,000-square-foot "healing center" that is enlivened by pleasing colors, artwork chosen by the patients themselves, an air-filtration system designed to be a hundred times more efficient than conventional systems against dust, germs, and other contaminants, and plenty of natural light from windows and skylights, even in surgery. The facility's fluorescent lights – flashing imperceptibly at 30,000 times per second – have a calming, not stressful, effect on patients and staff. Closed-circuit "care channels" carry healing music and video images developed specifically for the hospital.

The building itself is positioned so that its front door points to the mountains while the rear opens to the power-giving peak of Mauna Kea.

. . .

Among the most gratifying aspects of a miracle, of course, is the fact that it wasn't supposed to happen. So it was with the North Hawaii Community Hospital, which some people said would never get built and could never function, if it did get built, the "crazy" way its planners promised.

But what bright idea, what amazing vision, what worthy project has not had its nay-sayers? Before I became involved in the NHCH development, organizers had received from the state of Hawaii an offer of $12.5 million for a new health-care facility. The community had to match that amount, however, and, by the late 1980s, had raised only $4.5 million. We were told, then, we would never come up with the rest of the money. We were also informed that even if we did raise the necessary funding, we would never attract the critical mass of doctors and other health-care professionals we would need to properly staff the facility. Finally, we were told it would be difficult to receive the essential Certificate of Need (CON) from the state of Hawaii that would allow us to proceed.

But, as they usually are, the nay-sayers were wrong. In 1992 alone, we were able to raise $12.7 million – most of that amount coming from generous pledges from the likes of the Parker Ranch, a historic and very successful Big Island cattle operation, and other enthusiastic business interests, institutions, and families on the island. Even Honolulu-based Queens Hospital, the state's largest, pledged a million dollars toward the NHCH. As for the doctors, within a short time of our announced decision to go ahead with the project, we received several dozen applications from physicians all over the United States, men and women of all ages and a variety of disciplines, sharing (if nothing else) an ardent desire to practice a more patient-centered medicine than they could in their current positions. The CON was duly granted.

The hospital's staffing may have been the most miraculous part of this miraculous story. The interest among professionals from all over the United States (and from abroad as well) has been incredible. I can't explain it, except to say it's been a miracle; it's been divinely decreed. Despite the extraordinary natural beauty of the Big Island, we're a rural area, after all, relatively poor, and offering none of the man-made attractions of the big metropolitan areas where most U.S. hospitals are situated. But, despite warnings to the contrary, we began hearing from allopathic internists and family practitioners early on in the process. We were then told that we wouldn't get the specialists we would need. But, lo and behold, the specialists have come, too: an excellent cardiologist, for example, an outstanding gynecologist, and wonderful surgeons, among several others.

A particularly memorable episode involved a neurosurgeon from Michigan, whom I had known from my days at Medtronic. One day not long ago the surgeon and his wife happened to be vacationing on the Big Island. Because of our earlier relationship, they came to visit Doris and me at Waimea. Naturally enough, I took him on a tour of the new hospital (which had just opened its doors). A month later he called me from Michigan and said he was heading back our way. When, somewhat surprised, I asked him why he was returning so soon, he said he'd sold his home and was planning to work at the NHCH!

Our outstanding executive team leader (we don't use the old-fashioned hierarchical titles common to most hospitals), a very talented administrator named Patrick Linton, came to us from Wisconsin, but about 90 percent of the NHCH staff, excluding our physicians, are local. Many of our nurses worked in state-run hospitals, but many just seemed – again, almost miraculously – to come out of nowhere. There are so many wonderful, caring people here who seemed to have been waiting for this opportunity, I can't help but think there's been a greater power bringing us all together.

One of the recent innovations we employ here makes the most, we believe, of our excellent staff. It is called a "care team," which literally brings our primary nurses, aides, and housekeepers together in groups of five. Each team is capable of taking care of eight patients, a small enough number to allow the kind of close, personal contact among staff and between staff and patients that we believe is desirable. This system requires, of course, that nurses learn to perform multiple tasks, from, say, administering an electrocardiogram to performing various types of blood work. But it results in a closer relationship with patients, who, in a more conventional hospital, have to deal with several different nurses during a shift, increasing the apparent impersonal nature of their hospital stay.

Skeptics, understandably, point to such innovations and insist that adding complementary therapies to allopathic medicine will inevitably increase the cost of care. And isn't one of our stated objectives to contain rising hospital costs?

My response is that our way won't increase the cost of care – that, in fact, when all systems are operating at their optimal level, the NHCH will be a model of efficient and cost-effective diagnosis and treatment. In the conventional hospital, for example, about 40 percent of salaries go to people who aren't actually performing their assigned function at any given time. Because of over-specialization, those employees may be very active for two or three hours, but the rest of their shift comprises a great deal of downtime. Our cross-trained, multi-functional staff members are kept busy and on-task throughout their shifts.

There's also the issue of hospital design. The flow of patients from one function to another, though extremely important, was not a high priority in the design of most conventional hospitals, built decades ago. Visitors from other institutions say they can't get over the efficiency of our layout, as patients are transported swiftly from, for instance, the emergency room to our radiology station to intensive care, with minimal "traffic jams" and delays. When completely in place, our computerized record-keeping – created from scratch, without labor-intensive and time-consuming conversion from paper files – should also result in sizable savings. And complementary procedures and provisions can be significantly less costly themselves. When we were initially stocking our pharmacy, for instance, we spent $400,000 on allopathic drugs, while putting out only $30,000 for a similar quantity of herbal medications.

Still, to some people, much of what we're doing here on the Big Island is just plain crazy. Maybe they're right – which doesn't mean we shouldn't be doing it. Do patients really care about the pictures hanging in their hospital room? If they're sick enough, they probably don't. But if they're not – if they're like the majority of patients to whom an overnight stay in a hospital room is frightening and uncomfortable – a choice of a particular watercolor landscape may be important indeed. Our very first patient was a woman who was having elective surgery. Two days before the scheduled procedure she came in and, from the hospital's collection (all of it created, by the way, by local artists), picked out the paintings she wanted in her room. Selecting the artwork that brightened her personal space may have been a small item in the overall scheme of things, but it's one of several ways of giving the patient a sense of comfort, participation, and control over her hospital stay.

The bottom line will be the long-term cyberphysiological outcomes – from the patient's point of view, not from ours. This is what will ultimately decide how effective we are in providing a new kind of medicine, as a new kind of healing center. This is what health-care professionals all over the world will be watching. Toward that end we have been developing methods for measuring those outcomes. As I indicated earlier, it won't be the patients' physiological measurements that matter most, but how they believe their overall quality of life (or HRQL) has been affected by the healing process. Developing such measurements is a time-consuming, costly process in its own right. Quality-of-life indices have to be adjusted for different cultures and different diseases, among other variables. But that indexing is essential for us to prove to the world that integrated healing is the right tack for the 21st-century hospital.

As I write this, we are staffed for complete operation of 35 patient rooms. That translates into more than 280 good jobs for the local community. When, in another year, all of our rooms are full, employment should reach at least 300. We know that bringing good jobs to the Big Island contributes to good health and a vibrant community. Thus, if we do what we say we're going to do, the NHCH will mean a great deal not only to the physical, mental, and spiritual well-being of the community, but to the community's social and economic health as well.

. . .

As excited as we are about our hospital, we're also convinced that the NHCH is only the beginning of a much larger enterprise that could rejuvenate the entire island while offering a whole new concept of health care to the world. I'm speaking now of a concept we call the "Healing Island." Now that the hospital is up and running, I'm devoting most of my time here at home to helping make that dream a reality, too.

What is a Healing Island? It is clearly many things to many people (many dreams to many dreamers!), but its formal steering committee (which has since been succeeded by a strong board) developed the following statements of Vision and Mission:

A Healing Island in harmony with itself and the world.

Its mission is to communicate the range and quality of current and developing resources to the people of Northwest Hawaii, the state of Hawaii, and the world; to acquire resources and values in health, healing, and wholeness that are blessed by the spirit of the traditional culture of Hawaii; and to establish a reputation for Northwest Hawaii as a place of beauty and healing where people may, in the spirit of aloha, achieve self-realization and contribute their best to other individuals, society, nature, and the land in exchange for a meaningful, happy, and satisfying life.

Currently at various stages of discussion or development are several key components of the Healing Island, including a Five Mountain Medical Community comprising the North Hawaii

Community Hospital, Tutu's House (a community resource center for health education and counseling), a hospice, spas and other health-and-fitness resources (in conjunction with local hotels and resorts), spiritual retreats, and clinics of many specialties attracted to the area. According to a statement in our *Healing Island* quarterly journal (published by the Archaeus Project), "Such a Center, offering patient-empowered, integrated health care in the most attractive healing environment in the world, located at the crossroads of the Pacific, could add a major new dimension to the status and economy of Hawaii in the world community. The Center could provide a dramatic new model for healing of historical significance – a 21st-century Kos of the Pacific."

Kos is an island in the Aegean Sea where, more than 2,000 years ago, Hippocrates, the father of Western medicine, established a medical center and school: the original Healing Island. As several of us north Hawaiians focused on the idea of the Big Island as a healing center incorporating a holistic approach to health and medicine, the parallels to the Kos of Hippocrates struck us as dramatic. Both, for instance, are volcanic islands. Both offer (or offered, in the case of Kos) a hospital combining the latest technological and cyberphysiologic therapies. Both offer (or offered) patient-centered healing in a healthy climate, with a deep and abiding concern for sacred sites and the spiritual health of the community. The establishment of a healing center at Kos took place, moreover, at a time of epochal upheaval in philosophy, politics, science, and medicine, followed, shortly thereafter, by the arrival of the Christian message of spiritual rebirth and renewal. A time of change and promise, we believe, not unlike our own.

We believe, further, that our corner of the Big Island has an opportunity to provide the world of the 21st century a striking new model of health-care delivery. Our goal is to develop nothing less than a whole new paradigm for healing and health care, while providing a thousand new jobs, adding unprecedented vigor to the local economy, and enhancing the local quality of life.

To provide such a model – to establish such a paradigm – we believe we must re-focus health-care resources, from health-care professionals to the public itself, on the responsibility of each person for his or her health and wellness. As a matter of fact, a crucial element of the NHCH's mission statement is "empowering patients and families to become actively involved in their own health-care choices, by providing educational support to enable and encourage self-determination and responsibility in making health-care choices and pursuing healthy lifestyles." The Archaeus Project's words on the subject can well serve as a call to arms, at least as far as our Healing Island concept is concerned:

The proposed Healing Island "model rests on a return to self-responsibility, and its success depends on the involvement of family and community, on education, and on developing incentives and understandings that will inspire healthy behaviors in this region. This approach promises striking improvements in health statistics and cost containment.

"What is now needed is an insurance product based on this model that will support and promote this vision. To a system based on mechanistic philosophy and the well-defined technological hardware and techniques of modern Western medicine, the benefits of changes in behavior, of family and community conditions, of good mental attitudes, and the good words of a kindly health professional must seem vague and intangible. Clearly, it is time to address preventive measures in health and medicine. The time has also come to develop an integrated medicine that combines the best of allopathic thérapies with the methods and skills discovered by complementary medicine. New approaches to problems of prevention and of self-regulation are being developed, and old approaches rediscovered. People are already implementing these approaches to patient care. It is past time these new approaches be recognized within the insurance and governmental bureaucracies. Hawaii has done much to provide guidance toward the future of health care. It is completely possible that we can develop a model that will impact the rest of the nation and the world."

So, the miraculous little hospital that opened for business in the spring of 1996 is only part of the dream, of the vision, that we north Hawaiians have conjured for the Big Island. To develop a Healing Island on the foundation of that hospital is obviously a huge challenge, but surely not impossible if you believe, as I have come to believe, in spirituality and destiny.

TWO

High Tech, High Touch

To all appearances, it's been an unusual journey by an apparent anomaly: A reserved and reticent electrical engineer, a man of science and technology – a conservative Lutheran of Norwegian and Dutch ancestry hailing from a Snow Belt state – becomes deeply and passionately involved in spiritual healing, ancient therapies such as herbs and acupuncture, and other non-Western practices and traditions in the troubled paradise of rural Hawaii, and is now bound and determined to help create in his adopted home a Healing Island that can benefit the entire world, beginning with the 29,000 people who live on it.

You wouldn't think a person could get here from there. But I did. And if no one is more surprised by the route I have taken, no one is more pleased, either. I believe it's been a life well spent, if not particularly well planned.

And although the path from my Minnesota roots to my current preoccupations and activities in Hawaii has been circuitous, it has followed, to my eyes, a clear and irrefutable logic. I have been driven, I believe, by a heartfelt desire to use my knowledge and energy to help humankind. That desire was passed down to me by my parents and grandparents, who were great believers in goals and hard work and the acquisition of knowledge while actively serving their church (eventually my church). It was encouraged by my many wonderful teachers and then articulated by my pastor. The spark was provided, as I'll make clear a little later, by a Saturday-afternoon movie when I was still a boy in knee-pants. My mature efforts were joined by my thousands of colleagues and collaborators at Medtronic, and rewarded in many ways by the countless medical professionals and patients who chose and have benefitted from the technologies Medtronic provided. Since our marriage in 1982, my wife Doris has been my personal guide, encouraging my

15

exploration of complementary medicine and awakening me to the mental, spiritual, and physical benefits of massage, acupuncture, and other healthful modalities.

Whatever the original source (or sources) of that desire, it has brought me here, where, now in my middle 70s, I am at peace with myself and my environment. To some folks I may seem, at least from a distance, a round peg in a square hole. The creator of the world's first battery-operated wearable cardiac pacemaker and one of the pioneers of the electronic implantable medical-device industry wholeheartedly embracing spiritual healing and other decidedly "low-tech" responses to what ails us as human beings may seem peculiar indeed. Some of my old neighborhood friends and co-workers from the early days of Medtronic, who will recall my natural discomfort among strangers, have no doubt wondered if this is the same Earl Bakken who speaks to large professional audiences on the benefits of holistic health care and who routinely begins business meetings in Hawaii with hand-holding, prayer, and a public unburdening of personal concerns. I have been described in my later years as a stranger in a strange land. From my point of view, however, that's a quibble. I'm a technical man in a spiritual land, yes; but like all human beings I'm a spiritual creature, too. And even a spiritual land can benefit from technology.

The truth is, the Hawaiian energy that animates me today does not represent a rejection of or a shift away from anything I've done or believed back in Minnesota. The aloha spirit and my concomitant belief in a holistic approach to healing and health is simply an addition to, and integration with, my long-held ideas, ideals, and philosophies.

I trust that the why's of my story – the reasons for the twists and turns of my journey – will become clear, or at least more understandable, as this narrative progresses. For now, though, let me explain what I've been up to since settling down on the Big Island of Hawaii in the late 1980s, what I believe about healing and health care, and why I'm so passionately involved in the cause of the Healing Island.

· · ·

Not long after Doris and I moved into our adopted home on the Big Island, I set down my observations, thoughts, and beliefs on the integration of the healing arts and the healing sciences for a colloquium organized by the North Hawaii Community Hospital board and the Archaeus Project (which I described briefly in the previous chapter and will discuss further in Chapter 9). My feelings about the subject have only been strengthened by recent events, while being continually reinforced by the ideas and observations of several colleagues and loved ones, Doris foremost among them.

We have in Hawaii (I wrote) the opportunity to achieve something very special by building a healing center from the ground up. To be able to design a new hospital (as the healing community's first major component) and build it in such a way that will be appropriate to the medical demands of the new millennium was an exciting prospect indeed. Not only would this hospital (and eventually our multifaceted healing complex) provide high-quality care and good jobs for our community, it could serve as a demonstration project for the entire United States and the world.

For health care, this is (to borrow from Charles Dickens) both the best of times and the worst of times. In many ways it is the worst of times to be opening a new hospital, especially a small one, because small community hospitals are closing all over the United States. These hospitals are having trouble filling their beds and recruiting personnel. But it also the best of times because important, even revolutionary changes are taking place in medicine and health-care delivery. A new hospital and healing center – if designed, built, and operated with a new philosophy and new techniques – could make the most of those advances.

Everybody seems to agree that we're in the middle of a health-care crisis. Costs continue to spiral upward, despite efforts on the part of both the private and public sectors in the United States (and elsewhere) to contain them. Some progress has been made in some parts of the country (including the Twin Cities, back in Minnesota) to at least slow the ascent of health-care expenditures; but the pressure to do more with less weighs heavily on everybody and has a negative impact on the quality of care.

Several approaches have received widespread attention as means by which to contend with the crisis. These include managed care (health maintenance organizations, preferred provider organizations, and other much-discussed systems), outcome studies (to determine treatments appropriate to different patient populations), and regional initiatives (in which services are divided up and assigned to different hospitals within a given geographic area). Our approach at the North Hawaii Community Hospital would be, we decided, something entirely different. We called it "the 2010 concept."

The basic idea, simply stated, was to look ahead and forget about the health-care system that prevails today. The question for those of us planning that Healing Island became: What would the ideal health-care system look like in the year 2010? Suppose we had a magic wand and could whisk away the litigious environment and bureaucracy that are smothering so many of our best efforts today. Suppose we could determine much more than we know today about the nature of the mind in matters of health and disease, as well as about the critical healing factors borne by the patient's attitude. What sort of optimum health-care system could we then develop? If we could use our imagination and intuition – if we could conjure a vision of what this new world might be – we would have a goal and direction toward which to travel.

I chose the year 2010 because it was then (when I wrote that "manifesto") more than 20 "long" years away, assuming that few of us feel really threatened by prospects in a year so distant in the future. When we look out into the distant future, we are freer to imagine, to let our vision wander without fear of the possible consequences. The endless recommendations coming out of private and public studies, task forces, and commissions all seemed to agree that a fundamental restructuring of the system is necessary, but no one seemed to know quite how to go about it. Rationing, variations on a national health-care system, the weak promises of outcome studies – all of these seemed to be the result of too short a vision, too many limitations imposed by the way we look at the situation immediately at hand. We needed, I believed then, to take a longer view and let our minds wander. I believe we need to do that today.

. . .

Consider, for starters, the dichotomy of mind and body.

Suppose that on my left are the phenomena that involve the mind and to my right the phenomena that involve the body. Note that when we use the term "mind," we do not identify mind with brain. The mind is not entirely separate from the brain, but it is not a physical entity, as the brain is. Different people use different terms for the mind – consciousness or psyche, for instance. It is clear, at any rate, that each of our individual minds creates a more or less individual "reality." This is not to say that reality is entirely a product of individual consciousness, but that each of our minds perceives, interprets, and reacts to whatever "reality" in itself might be through the medium of a vast, and largely unconscious, reservoir of personal experience combined with a particular social and cultural background. Such variations in the interpretation of "reality" cannot be reduced to issues of chemical and physical reactions, and they have the greatest implications for individual response to health and diseases.

To my right, we have placed our notions about the body. We usually think of the body as a "machine" of which the mind is a noncausal, ineffectual epiphenomenon. We believe that every function of this flesh-and-blood "machine" eventually can be studied and elucidated. This is the reductionist viewpoint: If you look at finer and finer points down to cells and molecules, down to the atomic level, you're going to find that anything that is wrong with the body can be defined by some change in the physical structure of that body and, once having ascertained the causal chain leading to the disorder, you can develop and apply appropriate responses to the problem. Such a belief, however, is really as much a matter of faith as anything else, though it's what is generally called "scientific medicine" today. Yet if the body is perceived as a machine, then using scientific medicine and medical technology would seem to be the only rational way to deliver medical care.

All this, of course, has little to do with the mind. We aggressively treat the human body with surgery, drugs, and devices, and the mind is routinely left out of the equation. However, it is very interesting to note that technology usually works much better if the mind of the patient is made a part of the process. I know from my own work at Medtronic that we have much better results with certain devices when patients understand the device, believe in its effectiveness, and appreciate the implications of living with it inside them. Coming from the side of the mind, as is more often done in so-called humanistic or holistic medicine, we see something that incorporates a variety of medical practices that fall outside what is generally taught in medical school – therapeutic approaches with a long and successful history, such as nutrition, faith healing, massage, guided imagery, touch therapy, and home-opathy. Eastern medical techniques, such as moxa, acupuncture, and Ayurvedic medicine, are also used by holistic practitioners. I am especially interested in the approaches I refer to as "high-touch" therapies, which connect the mind with the body and help the body to heal.

Through research being done in biofeedback, hypnotherapy, psychoneuroimmunology, and a number of other "cyberphysio-logical" disciplines, we are learning a great deal more about the interaction between mind and body in both health and disease. On the technical side, we already know a lot about the body's organs and the systems that connect them – and this store of knowledge continues to grow at a rapid rate. We know less about the role of the mind. However, as our technological knowledge increases, it becomes more apparent that the mind is a greater factor in the equation than we (in the Western world) had supposed. As we learn more about mind and body, the links and interactions between them become more apparent. The best medicine for the patient, it is increasingly clear, combines these two general approaches in modalities that treat the problem of unwellness instead of discrete symptoms.

"The role of the mind" means that some of the effects that devices appear to produce may be due to the fact that they are serv-ing as powerful placebos. If that's the case, I say so be it. We are looking, after all, for beneficial results to the patient, not merely confirmation of our theoretical prejudices. A report not long ago in *The New England Journal of Medicine* stated that in some studies the transcutaneous electrical nerve stimulator (TENS device) worked no better or no worse on patient discomfort than a placebo. The implied conclusion was, Don't use either one. But was that an intelligent response? I don't think so. If the objective is to obtain beneficial results for the patient, it doesn't matter whether it's a placebo or a device – use it!

But this is a very difficult point of view to get across in Western medicine today, largely because Western medicine relies heavily on double-blind studies as a guarantor of efficacy. In my opinion, such studies in medicine have been the source of considerable harm. In double-blind studies you are leaving out of the picture the patient's mind, as well as the minds of the medical professionals providing the treatment. When you have left out the patient's state of mind along with a major part of the doctor's ability to convey trust and belief to the patient, practically nothing is going to work well. What we should strive for first in medicine is the result, and then study the mechanisms later. Sometimes, when I lecture at major hospitals about the fallacies of double-blind studies, doctors get up and walk out. But, interestingly, most of them do not. In truth, I don't mean to condemn double-blind studies; they serve a purpose and have an application. But we shouldn't let them blind us to what we really seek – namely, positive patient results and a significantly improved Health Related Quality of Life.

Technology has made tremendous strides during the past few decades. In 1940, there wasn't a lot of technology in medicine at all. Sure, there were a few well-known tools for a doctor to work with – stethoscopes, basic x-ray machines and techniques (although they weren't shielding the x-rays properly back then), and some minor testing devices – but that was about the extent of it. In those days, the doctor had to come to the patient's home, and what the doctor practiced more of then was the "art" of medicine: high touch, holding the patient's hand and touching his or her forehead, smoothing the sheets and adjusting the pillow, and adding the magic of words. Words were then, as they are now, powerful medicine. The patient trusted the physician, and the process of recovery developed out of a special relationship between the two (and the patient's family). This was not a "consumer-provider" relationship. The patient's mind was deeply incorporated into the healing process. True, there were many patients a physician couldn't save due to the lack of technology, but doctors generally achieved good results in spite of that deficiency. It must also be kept in mind that the greatest progress in the control of disease and extension of life expectancy derived from advances in sanitation, nutrition, and climate control, rather than from any specific technology.

As time went by – and really beginning during World War II – technology began to play a significant role in medicine. Eventually, when you walked into a hospital, you saw a great deal of equipment and machines – but very little touch therapy. Some doctors hadn't even been taught how to palpate a patient. All they knew was how to look at an electrocardiogram and read the reports that came back from the laboratory. They were often not interested in looking at the patient; the only thing that mattered were the x-rays and other test results. Technology was thought to solve all problems. When the results didn't turn out as expected, we used more technology to attempt to bridge the gap.

Recently, though, I have been seeing changes in the attitude of medical professionals toward high-touch care. Doctors are recognizing that the patient is more than a machine. Of course, there have always been doctors who understand that and practice medicine as an art. Unfortunately, they don't get paid for it. It's difficult to practice high-touch medicine extensively when there's no compensation for it. In spite of that problem, the use of high touch is now growing rapidly. Eventually, we will be able to combine the intelligent use of technology with high-touch techniques, incorporating the patient's mind into the healing process. We will learn to reach the "healer within," to turn on and support natural healing processes, understanding that the mechanism for activating the inner healer will not be the same for everyone. The movement toward high-touch medicine will have an effect on both the physical and administrative aspects of future hospitals and other health-care centers.

At the Archaeus Project we coined the term "cyberphysiology." *Cyber* derives from the Greek term *kybernetes,* referring to the helmsman of a ship, and points to the mind as the director, or helmsman, of the body. The term is used more and more, acknowledging the growing attention that's being paid to the interaction between mind and body.

One more good way to address the health-care crisis and build a new kind of healing for the 21st century – a cyberphysiologic way – involves generating greater patient satisfaction. The proper application of cyberphysiologic principles will mean that patients leave the hospital sooner. They will be satisfied with their care, so that the risk of litigation will be reduced even if the results are not everything they expected. Staff satisfaction is also an important factor, especially when it comes to recruiting and retaining first-rate personnel. As I travel around the United States telling people about our new hospital in north Hawaii, I find nurses and doctors everywhere saying, "I want to come, I want to join you." They perceive our new facility as an opportunity to return to the kind of practice that so many of them went into their professions to find, but have not been encouraged to practice. One of the big problems for a small hospital is to maintain the high occupancy rate that is required to remain solvent. If we have high patient satisfaction, doctors are going to refer patients to our hospital, and we can keep the beds filled. We have to change, moreover, the way caregivers are reimbursed for their services. We need to see that high-touch approaches to medicine are compensated. Until then, this kind of balanced high-tech, high-touch medicine is premature. Physicians are already moving toward this way of practicing medicine, but we have to prepare the ground for it.

We need to learn from others who are doing innovative things – from the Planetree organization in San Francisco, for example – so the best of the new approaches to patient-centered care, holistic therapies, and hospital design can be shared and incorporated into new projects. We need to know exactly what kind of medicine we're talking about and the impact of that practice on both the patient and the care-giver. This knowledge will be essential to building a whole new approach to healing long before 2010.

. . .

Our plan, through the Archaeus Project, was to devise a system that would provide optimum health care for our north Hawaii community by the year 2010. We felt if we could implement all we knew about health and sickness care, the result would look very different from the care we commonly see delivered today. It would reflect our knowledge of such phenomena as the difference between relief of symptoms and true cure, the interdependence of mind and body as well as mind and environment, the innate ability of the body to heal itself, and the curative effect of a positive relationship between the patient and the health-care professional.

Once we defined our vision for an optimum health-care system by 2010, we needed to determine the means necessary to make it a reality. We needed to seek, we believed, an effective balance between high-tech therapies and the healing that takes place within the complex relationship of mind and body. We needed to learn how to activate this dormant potential for healing. Neither technology nor high touch alone is sufficient; properly applied, however, technology can give direction to the body's healing processes. In such a supportive role, technology will continue to hold an important place in the medical armamentarium, despite its high cost and its sometimes inappropriate application.

Unfortunately, in the past several decades, we have proceeded as if our technological interventions and medications operated independently of the minds of either the patient or the doctor, though the mind, as we've come to recognize, can modulate the effects of a device or drug in a very positive way. Likewise, the device or drug may elicit healing powers from the patient.

We decided we must cultivate a new class of health-care professional who has the ability to diagnose by sight, smell, and feel as well as by high-tech devices, and to heal by touch (as well as by device and drug) in the wonderful bedside-manner tradition of the old-fashioned family doctor. Our high-tech capabilities can complement such skills, and will function all the more effectively because they are administered not with the cold, uncaring approach of an indifferent technologist, but with the warmth and concern of a familiar care-giver. Our machines and devices will work best when the patient willingly and optimistically participates in the treatment. When all of these conditions are right, the effectiveness of medicine in the 21st century may well exceed anything we currently imagine.

Project 2010 has also been looking for ways to reduce the cost of litigation, so precious resources would not be wasted in the practice of defensive medicine. Malpractice continues to be a real problem, of course, and patients must be compensated for damages resulting from medical incompetence, but the awards have to be kept in scale. We continue to seek ways to trim regulatory and bureaucratic overhead as we reform our reimbursement policies.

At the heart of our reform efforts is a deceptively simple plan called the tax-exempt Medical Savings Account, or MSA. The MSA concept is patterned after that of the extremely popular Individual Retirement Account, combining, in this case, a high-deductible health insurance policy with an employee savings account. For medical expenses costing less than the deductible (say, $3,000 to $4,000), a participating employee can draw from the savings account. What is left in that account at the end of the year can either be given to the employee or rolled over in the account.

Medical Savings Accounts, to our thinking, provide a win-win opportunity to eliminate managed care, with its wrongheaded emphasis on supply, and replace it with a much more practical –

and humane – reimbursement mechanism based on the control of demand. Employers can save significant health-insurance dollars because employees are encouraged to seek medical care only when they really need it. Employees, for their part, are rewarded physically and financially for their preventive measures (smoking cessation, diet and nutrition, regular medical exams, immunization, etc.) and for staying healthy. The only real losers are the insurance companies. Already close to 2,000 companies throughout the United States are allowing employees to take advantage of MSAs, and a dozen states have exempted the plans from state taxes. At this writing, the President and Congress have not bought into the idea, but we believe that MSAs are the only real solution to the reimbursement mess in the foreseeable future. In fact, we're starting our own MSA here in Hawaii.

For all of that, however, it seems abundantly clear that nothing is more important than a return to personal, human-to-human health care. We need to re-establish trust among doctor, nurse, and patient. True rapport is an essential ingredient in enlisting the power of the healer within. The right touch, the right words, the right expression can all act with the beneficial power of a wonder drug. In China, diagnoses have traditionally been made from the condition of the patient's pulse. The doctor sits across a table from the patient, taking hold of both of the patient's hands to feel the pulse at the wrists. The doctor may sit with the patient in this manner for half an hour, listening to the patient talk, looking at his or her color, feeling the pulse. Such a procedure has therapeutic power in its own right, and, like much of Eastern medicine, tends to encourage treatment of the patient's problem (physical, mental, or spiritual) instead of individual symptoms. In the United States, by contrast, it sometimes seems as though we'd prefer the patient be tended to by a computer.

At the Archaeus Project we have been advocating the concept of cyberphysiological healing. This comprises a wide range of techniques and phenomena that appear to be able to affect a variety of "autonomous" physiological functions in profound and specific ways. It includes the disciplines of psychoneuroimmunology and autogenics, the phenomena of biofeedback and hypnotherapy, the symptomatology of multiple personality disorders, and the practice of meditation, yoga, and similar techniques that can influence a person's consciousness.

There is also the very important concept of chronobiology, which refers to the relationship of our minds and bodies to time, to the cycles and rhythms that relate to our physical and mental activities, and to the parameters of our physical activity. Chronobiology concerns itself with how changes in time of day, day of the week, and week of the month affect our minds and bodies. Perhaps we are born chronobiologically "tuned" and then are wrongly taught to believe that there is a division between mind and body that leads to abstraction of experience. Maybe small children need to be encouraged to preserve their natural adaptations. An acute awareness of these patterns and fluctuations can greatly improve our understanding of physical ailments. The measurement of blood pressure is a prime example of the need for a chronobiological approach to health care. It's been estimated that fully half of the treatment for high blood pressure in the United States is unnecessary. Many of those treated for the disease were simply measured at the wrong time of day. Conversely, many others who do have high blood pressure may go untreated because measurements are not taken at a time of day when their blood pressure is elevated. I myself have been a "chronobiologist" for more than 40 years and have learned a great deal about these essential time-body dynamics in work with Professor Franz Halberg at the University of Minnesota.

I believe the eventual integration of cyberphysiology and chronobiology into conventional Western, or allopathic, medicine will by itself help improve health care dramatically. Indeed, physicians will someday look back on the way medicine is currently practiced and wonder why such fundamental aspects of human functioning were not routinely taken into account. The costs of implementing the techniques associated with cyberphysiology and chronobiology are negligible, because, once learned, they can be practiced independently, without medical supervision. More important, the consistent use of such techniques can significantly augment the quality of patients' lives.

I want to emphasize our belief that the techniques of cyberphysiology and chronobiology are not intended to replace conventional medicine. We are not, strictly speaking, looking for alternatives to current care. We are advocating significant adjunctive and complementary approaches to the medicine we know now – a powerful combination of the best of both high-tech and high-touch therapies.

. . .

My journey has been – and continues to be – not a narrowing of perspective like a railroad track receding in the distance, but a widening of scope and possibility, like the rising of the sun above vast Mauna Kea.

If I've learned one thing over the course of my journey – in fact, I've learned far more than I'll ever be able to convey in the pages of this book – it's that everything is connected. "No man is an island," the poet said. Every one of us is linked to every other, we live interdependently with our environment, and the success of our endeavors, great and small alike, rests not only on our own individual efforts, but on the strengths and conditions of those around us.

The idea of the human body being composed of independently functioning organs is a trick of the language. The body is "one," and every impact affects the whole. It is fruitless, similarly, to speak of improving the health of our Big Island community without effecting positive change in the family life, education and employment opportunities, and social conditions of our citizens. A high unemployment rate, for example, results in emotional and pyschological stress, diminished health, family dysfunction, alcoholism, drug abuse, and crime. By itself, the most innovative health-care center in the world won't create a truly healthy population; that care community must operate within a culture of loving families, strong schools and good jobs, and a caring, cohesive community in which everybody plays a valued role.

One of our happiest discoveries upon arriving in Hawaii is what I'll call here the Tutu phenomenon. In native Hawaiian culture, Tutu is your grandmother, who, by virtue of her age and experience, is a keeper of much knowledge, good sense, and love. When you are troubled or ill, you go to Tutu's house for counsel and comfort. Before we'd opened our new hospital in Waimea, we made sure we had established our own Tutu's House, where the entire community could come for education and outreach.

At Tutu's House we offer not only the highly effective touch of the wise elders on the staff, but a great deal of information (in both printed and video format) about health, disease, and other important subjects. Computers allow visitors to surf the Internet, with the capability to draw on more than 100,000 medical Web sites and plot their own "health map." Tutu's House is also the site of an ongoing series of special community-oriented programs covering everything from healthy diet to cancer and diabetes support to teenage parenting to playing the ukulele and hula dancing. Typical of the programs offered here was the recent presentation by Papa Henry Auwae, a Waimea native who is recognized around the world for his knowledge of Hawaiian healing herbs.

Tutu's House is a very special place where that interdependence among the diverse aspects of personal and communal life is recognized and served. It plays a critical role in empowering our people, giving them the information, skills, and self-confidence they need to take charge of their health and well-being. Tutu's House has been open for six years now, and I'm convinced that it has been the essential building block for the rest of our programs. For without an informed, educated, and empowered population, even the best-intentioned community plans will likely come to nothing.

Looking back now on my own beginnings, to my boyhood home in snowy Minneapolis, I sometimes think I've come a long way – yet, when I think again, I'm not so sure. We're always connected to our pasts, no matter how many zigs and zags our paths have taken, and so, in ways not always apparent, our pasts presage what lies ahead. I didn't have a Tutu's House way back there in Minnesota, but I did have a warm, loving home and wise, caring mentors.

And though I didn't think in such terms at the time, I was even then making high-tech, high-touch connections.

THREE

Electricity and Life

I've always been fascinated by electricity.

My interest in the phenomenon goes back farther, in fact, than I can remember. My mother told me that when I was a toddler, I was attracted to electrical cords, plugs, and connectors. Back then, during the 1920s, a home's electrical wiring often ran along the outside of the interior walls, and, according to my mother, I was especially interested, as a very small boy, in the porcelain insulators that protruded from the wall. Who knows why? Maybe because they were so white and shiny. Maybe because they seemed mysterious, with no obvious reason for being there. At any rate, one of my uncles, who happened to be an electrician, thought my interest in electricity was dangerous. He told my mother in no uncertain terms that she should stop me from playing with those cords and equipment.

"That boy's going to electrocute himself someday," he warned her sternly.

Needless to say, my mother didn't stop me. Rather than attempt to stifle or redirect my curiosity, she encouraged it. As a result, I have her, more than anyone else, to thank for this story.

. . .

My mother, born Florence Hendricks, was of Dutch and English extraction. My father, Osval Bakken, was pure Norwegian, both of his parents having come here from Norway. When I was growing up in Columbia Heights, in the northeast corner of Minneapolis, Minnesota, our Norwegian heritage seemed to play the most important role, in part because my father's family lived in the neighborhood and in part because we belonged to the nearby First Lutheran Church of Columbia Heights, where my father had been the first confirmand. We were all very active in that church. (I'm still enrolled there as a member.) With its emphasis on fundamental Norwegian Lutheran teachings, it had in fact an enormous influence on my life. It's also the place where I learned to eat lutefisk, a winter-time dish of lye-soaked cod that's considered a delicacy among Scandinavians.

Grandfather Lars Bakken had been, I believe, a military-equipment designer back in Norway. During the brief time I knew him, he always seemed to be sketching plans for one sort of mechanical device or another. I don't know if anything ever came of those drawings – I was told he liked creating variations of two-wheeled vehicles – but he sure seemed preoccupied by what he was doing. I remember going over to his house with my parents. He'd always come down from his study and say hello, but then he'd go right back upstairs to work. I was also told he was a first-rate mathematician, who wrote a book, in English, on algebra. Unfortunately, both he and Grandmother Bakken passed away when I was very young, so what little I know about them relies on dim memory and hearsay.

On my mother's side of the family, my grandfather John Hendricks also passed away when I was very young. Grandmother Eva Hendricks, however, lived right next door to us on 37th Avenue Northeast. Despite her advanced age, I remember thinking how modern and up-to-date she was because she owned a telephone at a time when most households didn't.

I was born in 1924. I was not quite an only child – but almost. My sister, Marjorie, was born when I was 18 and on my way into the service, so the two of us, though siblings, grew up separately, almost a generation apart. Thus, to all intents and purposes, I had the run of the house when I was a kid. My father was quiet and gentle, an avid reader who was addicted to crossword puzzles. He'd attended Augsburg College in Minneapolis for a couple of years, and, during most of my childhood, he worked as a clerk for a farm-implement supply company. My mother, who attended business school after high school, was proficient in math and served as our church's secretary. She also taught Sunday school and played the church organ at one time.

It was my mother who was always encouraging my scientific interests and who pretty much gave me the green light to do what I wanted, in and outside the house. In retrospect (and as a parent myself), I have to believe the freedom she allowed me was remarkable. Maybe she enjoyed my enthusiasms as much as I did. Those firecrackers on the Fourth of July, for instance. I used to wire them up and set them off electrically from a perch in an attic window. I also built a telephone system that stretched across the street to a friend's house. We'd scavenged the wire we needed from a blasting operation at a nearby sand pit and borrowed the earphones from Grandma Eva. Mother was skeptical about that last project, at least at first. She didn't believe our private phone system worked until the day she tried it herself and was surprised to be able to chat with my friend's mom on the other side of the street.

Nothing seemed to alarm my mother, though it's possible, I suppose, that she may not have known about everything I did. My pals and I liked to play with blasting caps, for instance, detonating the duds we'd found at the sand pit by putting them on the streetcar tracks. Those caps would go off with a tremendous bang and actually lift the passing streetcar off the tracks a little bit. We liked to hang out in a clubhouse we'd built under a nearby railroad bridge, and would hop the trains going slowly uphill near Columbia Park and ride them out to Lake Johanna, where we'd go swimming on summer afternoons. We industriously dug tunnels, too, some of them very elaborate, with several rooms. We'd crawl into those tunnels in the evening, cook potatoes, tell each other ghost stories, and have a high old time until our parents decided that such subterranean adventures were too perilous even for us.

Though I didn't have a sibling at the time, I had a wonderful group of close friends in the neighborhood, including Harry Zook – who eventually married my cousin, Norma Haversack, and who still lives in Columbia Heights – and my erstwhile telephone correspondent across the street, Joe Colianni. Looking back to those sweet days with my pals, I sometimes wonder if today's kids, with their cable television and electronic games, have even half as much fun as we did. Frankly, I doubt it.

. . .

I don't recall either one of my parents ever nudging me toward one particular career path or another. They were always emphatic, however, about the value of a good education for me and, later on, my sister. And while they would never have the money to buy their kids college educations, they always kept us supplied with the kind of toys and materials that were helpful to our development. The so-called educational toys I remember best included an electric-eye kit, a chemistry set, a microscope, several Erector Sets, electric trains, and Lincoln Logs. To me, those playthings were pure excitement and fun. I didn't realize until later how important they were in providing me with a hands-on appreciation of electronics, chemistry, biology, physics, and engineering.

To supplement the store-bought toys, Mother used to scour the neighborhood for the raw materials I needed for my electrical and radio-building hobbies. She didn't have much money to spend, so she would go into hardware stores and radio shops seeking used and cast-off parts. That meant copper wire, vacuum tubes, switches, dials, knobs – you name it. She was always bringing that stuff home. I don't believe she had any long-term objective in mind for me. I think that most of all she just wanted me to have what she knew would make me happy.

Whatever else I fiddled around with in those days, my abiding interest was electricity. In my beloved basement workshop I fussed with electrical connections for all kinds of devices, experimented with batteries, and early on entertained myself by assembling simple devices like electrically activated bells and buzzers. Eventually, I moved on to more complicated "products," the most notorious of those being a couple of robots built with Erector Set parts and stray pieces of plywood. One of those robots was a fairly elaborate, five-foot-tall construction that blinked its eyes, talked (via a remote-controlled speaker), and puffed on hand-rolled cigarettes! (For its lungs I used a hot-water bottle, which the tobacco smoke rotted out from the inside and thereby furnished me another important lesson for life: Stay away from cigarettes!) As a gag one Halloween, I had that robot brandish a knife. Well, a blinking, talking, cigarette-puffing robot was one thing. A knife-wielding "monster" was another. The latter scared the wits out of a neighbor boy who claimed he was "attacked" by the thing, and I was ordered by my parents to destroy it. There was, after all, a limit to what even the Bakkens would put up with.

In junior high and high school I was forever drawing plans for radios and rocket ships and futuristic houses with all the electrical wiring in place. (Echoes of Grandfather Bakken's sketches for the devices and constructions he played with in his mind!) I had a lot of good, nurturing instructors, and was especially encouraged by a pair of science teachers at Columbia Heights High School – the brothers Rodney and Russell Sahlstrom. Rodney Sahlstrom assured me that it was perfectly all right to be what kids today call a "nerd," and that a fellow didn't have to hang out in pool halls to have a good time. That was good news, because I was the nerd who took care of the public-address system, movie projector, and other electrical equipment at school. My one athletic interest was running track, for which I earned a varsity letter. When I wasn't running, I traveled with our football and basketball teams to help operate the electric scoreboards and loudspeaker equipment.

I was always near – but not quite at – the top of my high school class. My strengths, not surprisingly, lay in math and science, not in English and history. Science was, of course, my passion, and I enjoyed a little celebrity status as the kid who would sometimes get the teacher out of a jam. When a teacher was having trouble with this or that device or experiment, my classmates would chant, "Let Earl do it! Let Earl do it!" – and, red-faced but secretly tickled by the attention, I'd get up and do my best to straighten out the situation. I wasn't trying to show off, but I did love solving problems that had stumped the "expert." In the meantime, I just about memorized every book the school library carried on subjects relating to physics, biology, and chemistry. On one particularly memorable occasion – Monday, December 8th, 1941 – I modified a radio and connected it to the PA system so the principal could broadcast to the entire school President Roosevelt's request for a Congressional declaration of war against Japan.

I always liked to read. When I was little, I devoured all the Big Little Books and comics I could get my hands on. A little later, I pored over my *Popular Mechanics* and *Popular Science* magazines. But as voraciously as I read, and as excellent as my formal instruction proved to be, I believe that many of the most important lessons I learned were self-taught. That goes back, of course, to the hands-on education I'd received playing with those photo-electric kits and Erector Sets and fabricating those homemade telephone systems and robots.

At some point – I can't tell you exactly when – I realized I had an inventive capability, though I wouldn't have thought to call it that at the time. I remember, for example, messing around with a lawnmower that employed a rotating blade, long before there were rotary mowers on the market. I also developed a rudimentary version of what today we call a stun gun. I was fascinated by the way mechanical and electrical devices worked. I liked nothing better than tearing apart a tool or device or piece of equipment to see what made it tick, then reassembling it, perhaps with a little addition, modification, or improvement. One of the happiest memories of my happy childhood was coming home alone after Sunday school, sneaking into the house via the coal cellar while my parents were still at church, taking apart our new floor-model radio, and then painstakingly putting it back together before my folks arrived home for dinner.

One summer while I was in high school I was hired to help out in the office of a small manufacturing company in downtown Minneapolis. My job was to run the Ditto machine, but what really intrigued me was a mechanical calculator called a comptometer. During my lunch hours, I taught myself how to operate the machine, and by the end of the summer I was using it routinely as one of the firm's billing clerks.

To this day, I find a deep, almost inexpressible joy in the sight, sound, feel, and even smell of those old radios, machines, and electrical equipment. There is a magic about those devices that a person can appreciate only when he knows them inside and out, and when he loves them not only for what they do, but how they do it. Unfortunately, that kind of hands-on education and appreciation doesn't seem to be so easy to come by anymore, and I fear that many of our engineers and technicians are worse off for lacking it.

So much work today is performed with breathtaking speed and precision on a computer, yet the results are often incomplete and unsatisfactory because our engineers never get the sense of the actual object they're designing on a screen. They make faulty assumptions because they have never taken the real thing apart and put it back together again. They've never jiggled it in their hand, never gotten a feel for its density and heft, never lifted it to their nose and smelled it! What a pity for them – and maybe for the rest of us as well.

. . .

If, as I look back on my childhood so many years later, there was a single, defining moment that might have predicted the career that followed, the moment occurred one Saturday afternoon in the early 1930s. I was eight or nine years old and a regular at the Saturday matinees at the Heights Theater on Central Avenue in Columbia Heights, where my pals and I watched all the terrific movies and serials of the time.

My favorites were those incredible science-fiction films – we called them "horror shows" – in which electricity, usually applied by a "mad" scientist, rendered someone supernaturally strong, invisible, or in some other astonishing way changed.

Foremost among those films was *Frankenstein,* the unforgettable story of the learned doctor who, through the "magical" power of electricity, gives life to a collection of inanimate body parts. Misunderstood and tormented by "civilized" society, the doctor's spectacular creature turns into a "monster" who inspires terror across the countryside. The film was (and continues to be – it's been made at least 30 different times) a gripping masterpiece that's excited the imagination of several generations of moviegoers. Yet what intrigued me the most, as I sat through the movie again and again, was not the monster's rampages, but the creative spark of Dr. Frankenstein's electricity. Through the power of his wildly flashing laboratory apparatus, the doctor restored life to the unliving.

At those Saturday movies of my youth I also saw in dramatic operation the shipboard radios, telegraphy, and other electrical technologies I had until then only read about in books and magazines. But it was the restorative energy of electricity that excited and, eventually, inspired me. Many years would pass, of course, before I became aware of the use of electricity, electrical devices, and even electrically charged sea creatures for medical purposes, and that the understanding of the relationship between electricity and human life dates back far beyond Mary Shelley's 19th-century tale of the doctor and his monster, at least to Roman physicians of antiquity. For the time being, I was simply awestruck by the fact that electricity, properly applied, could do a great deal more than light up a room or ring a doorbell. I realized that electricity defines life. When electricity flows, we're alive. When it doesn't, we're dead.

Several years later, when I was confirmed, our pastor, Dr. Christofer Hagen, took me aside for a one-on-one conversation. Like most of the people who knew us in the neighborhood, Pastor Hagen was well aware of my passion for science and technology. On that occasion, by way of preparing me for life as a confirmed member of the church, he explained that science is neither good nor bad in itself. What's important, he said, is how science is used. He said it would be my responsibility, if I pursued a scientific career, to use it for the benefit of humankind and not for destructive purposes.

As much as I had concentrated on scientific and technological matters, I hadn't thought about science in moral terms. But I was still only a kid in my early teens. So the pastor's talk, while making me think, did not impress me as much as it would later. Then, like that *Frankenstein* movie of my childhood, his words would go a long way toward explaining the direction in which I would channel my efforts and what I would ultimately want to do with my life.

FOUR

Medtronic

When I graduated from high school in December 1941, I harbored no grand plans for a career. I knew I wanted to work with electricity. And, ever since that *Frankenstein* movie, I was particularly intrigued by the idea of somehow combining electricity and medicine. I'd also kept in mind the admonition of my pastor and was vaguely intent on doing something with my life that would be beneficial to others.

I was not what you'd call an outgoing guy. As a matter of fact, I was deeply introverted. Among my neighborhood buddies, I was often the leader of our apple-swiping forays and tunnel-digging adventures, but in the wider world beyond the familiar boundaries of Columbia Heights I thought I'd be perfectly happy losing myself in a laboratory. In fact, my dream job at that time was an anonymous research position deep in the heart of the Minneapolis-based Honeywell Company, which was then, as it is today, one of the premier electrical-technology manufacturers in the world (and, at that time, had a medical division).

War had broken out in both Europe and the Pacific by that time, however, and I decided that whatever I chose to do about a career would have to be put temporarily on hold. Because of my interest in radio communications, I enlisted in the Army Signal Corps and was enrolled, at Uncle Sam's expense, in a 90-day electrical-engineering course at the University of Minnesota in Minneapolis. Upon graduation, I was granted a first-class commercial radio-operator's license, then sent to Basic Training in Miami Beach, Florida. From there, I was shipped off to Camp Murphy, near West Palm Beach, and eventually wound up at the air base, in nearby Boca Raton, where I became a radar instructor. All told, I spent three years in Boca Raton, taught airborne radar maintenance, rose to the rank of staff sergeant, and discovered that I really liked to teach.

At the end of the war I returned to Minneapolis and, with the help of the G.I. Bill, began working toward my bachelor-of-science degree in electrical engineering at the University of Minnesota's Institute of Technology. When I'd earned the B.S., I began working toward a master's degree. The U of M, in the middle of the Twin Cities, was a bustling, exciting place, with a great deal of interesting programs and activities to engage the imagination of a curious young person. (It still is.) During my spare time, I used to wander across Washington Avenue to the University Hospitals, where I became acquainted with some of the people in their extensive labs and began providing, at their request, an ad hoc, on-the-spot repair service for malfunctioning equipment.

While I was in grad school, I married a bright young woman named Connie Olson, who had been in my class back at Columbia Heights High. Connie had studied medical technology while I was in the service, and by the time I got home she was already working as a medical technologist at Northwestern Hospital in south Minneapolis. Often, I'd run over to the hospital and wait for her to finish her shift. While I waited, I got to know several of the doctors and technical personnel there. Knowing that I was studying electrical engineering, they'd sometimes ask me if I would take a look at this or that piece of equipment that was giving them trouble. If I could fix the equipment, I would. It was a win-win situation. They were grateful, and I'd learn something about the machine. I didn't realize it at the time, but I had stumbled onto a career.

Actually, I'd already had a couple of irons in the fire by that time. Shortly after returning home from the service, for example, I got to know a group of young engineers who were all looking for a way to make a living. A few of us, with more enthusiasm than either capital or connections, started a phonograph-record company out of a fellow's garage on Selby Avenue in St. Paul. Calling our fledgling company Twinco, we briefly dared dream of becoming a big-time production company. We built our own recording equipment, cut some masters, and pressed a few records. We even had our own "artist" – a fellow known as Slim Jim, the Vagabond Kid, who sang Norwegian folk songs on local radio. Unfortunately, neither Twinco nor the Vagabond Kid set the world on fire. Before long, Twinco had abandoned record production and was installing and repairing car radios. At the last board meeting I attended, the group had decided they would get out of the car-radio business and get into the manufacture of squirrel traps. That's when I bailed out. And that was about the last I heard of Twinco.

Thankfully, there were other, less pressing, and more rewarding diversions, too. Not long after we returned home, one of my engineer pals, Ben Winich, introduced me to some friends of his father, the Piccards, a family of well-known hot-air balloonists, who lived in a big, handsome house on the River Road in Minneapolis. On Sunday afternoons the Piccards opened their home to a fascinating mix of academics, professionals, and other thoughtful people for fellowship and conversation. What a pleasure those Sunday afternoons were! What a marvelous opportunity to hear intelligent people talk, brainstorm, and go off in all different philosophical directions.

For a young man brimming with ideas and enthusiasm of his own, the new peacetime world was wide open and nearly everything seemed possible.

. . .

Hospitals and doctors' offices in the late 1940s were not the temples of technology they are today. Even excellent big-city institutions like the University and Northwestern hospitals had, by today's standards, limited and fairly rudimentary diagnostic and therapeutic equipment. A few of the more advanced electrical machines employed some of the nascent electronic technology developed during the war, but most of the devices were big, bulky, unwieldy things that still relied on the vacuum tube for their function. Nevertheless, the various flame photometers, colorimeters, electrocardiograph machines, and other electrical equipment played an important role in the diagnosis and treatment of patients and thus needed careful attention. The trouble was, few if any hospitals maintained a technical staff to keep their electrical equipment humming, so when a machine broke down, it would generally be hauled out to a local radio shop or shipped back to its manufacturer for service. There was, to my knowledge, no established businesses in the Twin Cities dedicated to medical-equipment repair.

One night in 1949 my brother-in-law, Palmer Hermundslie, and I were chatting at a family birthday party. Palmer was a kind, smart, engaging fellow, with an interesting background and an eye peeled for business opportunities. Married to my wife's sister, he was 30 years old, five years my senior. Like me, he'd grown up in Columbia Heights. Before and during the war he'd flown training missions for the Air Corps, and he still loved to fly. After the war he had worked briefly at Honeywell and was now helping run a lumberyard. At the party that night, our conversation got around to my occasional repair work at the hospital. It was pretty basic electrical stuff, I told Palmer, but there didn't seem to be anyone else who could fix those machines on the spot. Sure, there were the radio shops in town, but their business wasn't medical equipment. And shipping a machine back to its manufacturer was time-consuming and expensive, and the machine would be unavailable for weeks, if not longer. Palmer, with his nose for business, was intrigued by the scent of a fresh opportunity. The longer I talked, so, for that matter, was I. Pretty soon we'd both reached the same conclusion. Since there weren't any companies dedicated to medical-equipment repair, maybe there was an opening for a couple of bright young fellows like us.

On April 29, 1949, a few days after that discussion, Palmer and I formed a partnership to service electrical medical equipment. We called the company "Medtronic" – a contraction of *medical* and *electronic* that seemed a straightforward representation of our business – and set up shop in a garage at 818 19th Avenue Northeast in Minneapolis. The division of labor seemed equally logical and uncomplicated. Palmer was the businessman. He would run the office and manage the finances. I was the technician, so I'd hold down the shop and repair the equipment. In retrospect, I don't think either one of us viewed the business as a long-term proposition, much less a full-fledged career. Whatever Palmer had in mind regarding the future, I figured I'd be completing my master's work at the U of M, maybe going on to get my doctorate, then either teaching or settling down at that quiet research bench at Honeywell. I'd already had plenty of job offers, so even with a wife and plans for a family, I thought I could take a chance on running a little company.

Every entrepreneur, I'm sure, retains at least a few vivid memories of the early days of the business. I can still see that garage where we initially opened our doors and spent our first 12 years. The original structure was a railroad boxcar that had been modified and added onto by Palmer's family, who had used it for rebuilding cars. I don't know when that structure was built – before I'd come around, anyway. When we took it over, it was about the size of a three-stall garage. (The one stall that had still been used as a garage we designated our shipping-and-receiving area.) Though it had been insulated, the little building was very cold in the winter. On the coldest days, we'd huddle around an oil-burning stove, rub our hands together, and try to keep warm. Our first secretary, Goldie Benson, had to keep an electric heating pad between her feet and the icy cement floor. In the summer, the heat was suffocating. We used a garden hose to spray water on the roof in a not especially successful attempt to cool the place down a few degrees. At least once during those early days, the garage was infested with flying ants.

Even by start-up standards, the place was pretty crude. Outside it looked like what it was: a jerrybuilt boxcar-turned-garage-turned-repair shop. Inside there were only a couple of homemade desks and work benches and a jumble of the kind of tools, wires, tubes, dials, knobs, and so forth that you'd find in the back room of a radio shop or in a tinkerer's basement. On the positive side, the price was right. The Hermundslies didn't charge the company rent.

Despite the low overhead, Medtronic's beginnings were not auspicious. Our first month in business we grossed a grand total of eight dollars – for the repair of a centrifuge. We had no sense that we were planting the seeds of something big, either. We had no sense, for that matter, that we were doing anything remotely significant for humankind. All we were trying to do at the outset was scrape up enough business to make ends meet, to earn a modest living. It was a desperate struggle from the start. Thankfully, Palmer had some of his own funds to work with, and Connie was making enough money at her medical-technician's job to keep us fed and clothed.

Most of Medtronic's early business was repair work for local hospitals and doctors' offices, though we weren't so highly specialized that we wouldn't gladly work on a television set that needed fixing. Almost from the beginning we were doing some custom equipment-building as well. But we were naive, not sure about our "market," and making our way by trial and error. Palmer had some business experience, true enough, but medical electronics (even as rudimentary as it was in those days) was new to him. I knew most of the equipment and many of the people who used it, but I didn't know anything about building and operating a business. Everything we did at the beginning – and, indeed, for the next several years – we lost money on. We never figured out how to charge enough to make a profit on the service work; and what we built for customers would always end up costing us more than what we felt we could fairly charge them.

Still, not knowing any better, we persisted. We even began assembling a tiny staff when the volume of business allowed. Palmer did most of the hiring. Our first employee was a young electronics technician by the name of John Bravis. Dale Blosburg and his father, John, both of whom we'd known at church, were other early hires. When we needed a few extra hands, Palmer would sometimes round up a couple of souls from the local YMCA, although those fellows usually didn't work out as well as the folks we knew or found by word of mouth. In any case, there was little sense of team-building in those days. From their point of view, I doubt if any of those original employees believed they were signing on for anything more than a very short-term job.

In 1950, to supplement our exceedingly modest repair and equipment-building activity, we began selling equipment for other companies. We became a regional representative for the Sanborn Company, a Boston-based manufacturer of electrocardiograph machines, multi-channel physiologic recorders, and other, mostly diagnostic machines, and, a little later, for Gilford Instrument Company and Advanced Instruments, Inc. For the first time in my life I was functioning as a salesman. Despite my shyness, I discovered I liked selling more than I thought I would. I especially enjoyed connecting with people who needed what I was selling to help do their job, and felt a tremendous sense of accomplishment when I could use my engineering skills to tailor a piece of equipment to a customer's particular need. During this period, Palmer and I called on hospitals, clinics, and doctors' offices in Minnesota, the Dakotas, and parts of Wisconsin, Iowa, and Nebraska for Sanborn and other original equipment manufacturers.

As things turned out, of course, that manufacturer's-rep activity not only helped keep us in business (albeit only by a whisker); it also gave us an entree into the labs and offices of the doctors, nurses, and technicians whose needs, knowledge, and encouragement would be the basis for Medtronic's eventual growth and success.

. . .

Although we didn't fully appreciate its significance at the time, the late 1940s and early '50s would prove to be the dawn of a pivotal period in medical history. With the advent of the transistor (developed in the middle '50s), a variety of plastics, and other new synthetic materials, medical technology was on the threshold of several major breakthroughs that would dramatically transform the diagnosis and care of patients around the world.

Most of the new electronic equipment coming into the field during the early 1950s were monitoring devices and other diagnostic tools: EKGs, blood-flow machines, blood-gas shakers, cell counters, etc. There was still very little electronic technology designed and used for therapy. At that time we were selling a lot of other companies' recording devices for clinical animal labs in our territory. But, eventually, little by little, we were also getting into hospital surgical suites. Cardiologists at the University of Minnesota and other local heart centers, for example, were beginning to do some heart catheterization in the course of their pioneering work in open-heart surgery. After we would sell them, say, a multi-channel recording device for the cath lab, we would set up the equipment, help train the personnel in its use, and then be on hand to troubleshoot and repair it when necessary. We were, without really giving it a great deal of thought at the time, forging working relationships with physicians and their staffs that would soon have historic implications.

It would be fun to say that Palmer and I were visionaries who saw the brave new world of sophisticated medical technology spread out in front of us. In truth, however, we didn't see ourselves on the cutting edge of anything. We didn't realize how exciting the times were until we looked back on them later. (Even my near-electrocution while assisting with equipment during a U of M operation didn't seem quite so harrowing until viewed retrospectively.)

Still in our corporate toddlerhood, we were simply struggling to remain on our feet and grabbing at nearly any opportunity that came along.

At our makeshift headquarters in northeast Minneapolis, we were adding a technician or secretary to the staff when we could afford to and gradually increasing our work space. We expanded our operation into a second, two-stall garage on the Hermundslie property and then connected the two garages, adding a much-needed furnace and toilet to the structure. We also built an addition to the first garage, so the enlarged facility comprised a business area, shop, and even a little drafting room.

We'd become, in the meantime, a small, tightly knit family of six or seven men and women who liked our work even if we weren't overly confident about its future – and who liked each other personally as well. One of the simple pleasures of that time was gathering, the group of us, in Earl Hatten's drafting room and eating our brown-bag lunches while listening to an up-and-coming commentator named Paul Harvey on the radio. Some days we'd walk over to the Elmwood Cafe on Central Avenue, where there was no printed menu and nothing fancy in the way of either decor or food – only marvelous homestyle cooking that featured great breads and pies.

After five or so years in operation, Medtronic still wasn't much in the way of a business enterprise, but it was something, and when we weren't fretting about our survival we realized we were having a wonderful time.

FIVE

The Birth of an Industry

I suppose you could characterize the 1950s at Medtronic as years of discovery. We were – though I don't think we really appreciated or could have articulated it at the time – a company in search of a mission.

While our sales activity on behalf of Sanborn and other original equipment manufacturers pretty much kept us afloat, we were constantly building custom devices at the request of our growing number of friends and acquaintances within the Upper Midwest medical profession. If we weren't building new devices from scratch, we were modifying existing equipment or adapting it for new applications.

This was not, I can assure you, part of a formal business plan of any kind. We were simply looking for new business, new ways to bend our growing technological knowledge and professional relationships into profitable form. In fact, it was an admittedly hit-and-miss proposition. A doctor or laboratory technician would come to us and ask us to build, say, an esophageal monitor, or maybe a respirator for the animal lab. We'd say, O.K., and we'd build it. Sometimes we'd think it was pretty hot stuff, and hope that maybe another doctor or technician might want one like it. Unfortunately, in most cases only the original customer would share our enthusiasm for the product. There would be no other buyers. As a result, we never made more than a half-dozen or so copies of most of those devices. We never made any serious money on that early custom-building activity, either, rarely even recouping the cost of the prototype.

It was our extreme good fortune to be doing a lot of our repair and customizing work for the medical and research staffs at the University of Minnesota in Minneapolis. These included Dr. C. Walton Lillehei and his team of young surgeons who were, during the early and middle '50s, making significant strides in the promising new area of open-heart surgery. Lillehei's group might need, for instance, a customized recording device for an open-heart procedure. We would provide the device, set it up in their surgical suite, train the doctors in its use, then troubleshoot and repair it, if and when a repair might be necessary. Of course, we would be there with them in surgery when they were using it.

My relationships with the medical and research personnel at the university went back, as I explained earlier, to my days in graduate school, when I'd cross the street and visit my friends at the hospital. During Medtronic's formative years, I became a more or less regular fixture over there. As a matter of fact, I spent so much time in the offices, surgery suites, and animal labs at the U of M that I was given my own locker. I got to know people both personally and professionally, and learned as much as I could about their work. The anesthesiologists bought the early recording and monitoring equipment, and they introduced me to the surgeons.

I was an outsider – a non-physician – in their highly specialized and incredibly demanding world. But I think my independence was a quality they appreciated. If they had a problem with one of their electrical devices, I could often fix it immediately, freeing them from the hassle and delays of filing a request and pushing it through the institution's bureaucracy. Furthermore, I was about the same age as most of the interns and residents I'd met there, so we shared a lot of life experiences and attitudes common to members of the same generation. Later on, as it happened, many of those young doctors became prominent physicians and heads of surgery at hospitals around the world, thus giving Medtronic far-flung and influential contacts when we were in the pacemaker business.

But the global pacing business was still in the unseeable future. As far as I was concerned at the time, these were just a great bunch of talented men and women, fun-loving friends, and loyal customers who would call on Medtronic whenever necessary to perform a little "surgery" on their equipment.

. . .

In any case, it certainly never hurt an entrepreneur to be in the right place at the right time.

For Medtronic, the right place was the University of Minnesota Hospitals during the mid-1950s. In 1954, Lillehei began operating on infants – so-called "blue babies" because of the bluish tinge to their skin caused by insufficiently oxygenated blood – in order to repair congenital defects of the heart. The procedure, while effective, often interfered with the ability of the baby's heart to conduct the electrical impulses that sustain a steady beat, resulting in a condition known as "heart block."

To keep the tiny hearts beating after surgery, Lillehei had to rely on the big, alternating current-powered pacemakers that had come into use during the early 1950s. When we talk about cardiac pacemakers today, we think of devices as small as a silver dollar. Their AC predecessors, however, were large, bulky boxes filled with vacuum tubes that had to be wheeled around on carts and plugged into the wall. They were portable in name only, since they could only go as far as the nearest electrical outlet. Because of their bulkiness and AC-power requirement, no one thought of using them on patients except for only a short period of time. Still, those devices were effective, especially in emergency rooms, with patients suffering cardiac arrest, for example, and in certain other acute situations. For those pediatric heart-block patients, the machines provided a temporary assist that, in most cases, allowed the hearts to heal enough to conduct sufficiently on their own.

That AC pacemaker was, in fact, state-of-the-art technology at the time – the latest step in what had been to that point in history a slow, halting march dating back several centuries.

The core concept of pacing therapy – using an outside source of electricity to stimulate human tissue – was known to ancient Roman physicians, who treated gout-sufferers and other pain patients with electric rays and other electrically charged sea creatures. Cardiac pacing itself can be traced back to documented attempts to electrically stimulate the heart in the mid-1700s. Speculation about the bio-electric nature of the cardiovascular system had been published as early as the 1640s. By the end of the 18th century, there was general agreement that electricity had a pronounced effect on the heart. In 1791, the Italian scientist Luigi Galvani announced that electricity was inherent in organic tissue.

About the same time, another Italian, Alessandro Volta, demonstrated that electrical current could be produced from the contact of dissimilar metals. Volta gave the world its first battery for low-voltage, high-current stimulation.

Throughout the 19th century, physicians sporadically used rudimentary forms of electrical stimulation to treat cardiac disorders. Crude as the technology was at the time, however, it was ahead of Western medicine's understanding of heart disease. That lack of knowledge, plus the absence of any sort of standardized approach to the therapy itself, resulted in what seemed to be a bewildering range of effects. An English doctor, John MacWilliam, made a heroic attempt in the late 1800s to collect and analyze the scattered data then available on the subject. As incomplete as they were, MacWilliam's writings included the basic concepts of modern pacing and accurately identified many of the treatment's problems.

Shortly after the turn of the century, a technological breakthrough in Holland – the invention of the electrocardiograph – significantly increased our knowledge of the electrical workings of the heart. That knowledge led, in turn, to the development of the first devices specifically designed to artificially pace the heart. Credit for the first external cardiac pacemaker has been shared by two doctors – Australian Mark Lidwell and Albert Hyman of the United States – who, working independently, developed pacing machines during the late 1920s and early '30s. Lidwell's device ran on alternating current and required a needle to be inserted in the patient's ventricle. Hyman's, by contrast, was powered by a spring-wound, hand-cranked motor. Its electrical impulses – adjustable to 30, 60, or 120 per minute – were directed into the patient's right atrium through a bipolar needle electrode.

Not much is known about the outcome of Lidwell's efforts. We do know that Hyman's pioneering work was quickly frustrated and eventually derailed by technical problems and the attitudes of the times. Even as late as the 1930s, the medical and social environments were not ready for electrostimulation. Hyman was neither a quack nor a snake-oil salesman, but his pacemaker was roundly dismissed as "gadgetry" at best, the work of the devil at worst. He couldn't even find a manufacturer for the device. Interest in cardiac pacing languished until the early 1950s, when Dr. Paul Zoll, a Boston cardiologist who had been studying the work of the Canadian researchers John Callaghan, Wilfred Bigelow, and J.A. Hopps, developed an external pacemaker that was successfully applied to the treatment of heart block. By that time, research into electrostimulation was beginning to accelerate as new technologies (many deriving from war-related research) accompanied increased knowledge of the heart. Indeed, historian Kirk Jeffrey has written that the advances recorded by Zoll and others laboring in the field at that time created "the takeoff stage of cardiac pacing, a stage dominated by radically new devices invented by physician-led research teams working in teaching hospitals."

One such teaching institution was, of course, the University of Minnesota Hospitals in Minneapolis, where Walt Lillehei and his team of surgeons were treating blue babies suffering heart block. But Lillehei's reliance on those AC-driven pacemakers was an ongoing problem. Besides the machines' obvious limitations in portability, the therapy they provided was uncomfortable and often traumatic, especially for pediatric patients. Their effectiveness was also only as good as their external power supply. If the power failed, they were worthless.

On October 31, 1957, that's exactly what happened. For most Twin Citians, the sudden blackout was only a temporary inconvenience. For Lillehei's blue babies, the three-hour outage was a life-threatening event. (The hospital had emergency power generation in its surgery suites and recovery area, but not in its patient rooms.) Tragically, one baby died that night. And for worried caregivers the experience was another reminder of the limitations of existing technology.

The next day Lillehei asked me to see if Medtronic could come up with something better.

. . .

With 20-20 hindsight, it's easy to look back on that assignment and label it the crucial turning point in Medtronic's short history. At the time, though, it was simply another request from a valued customer. It was more urgent than most, sure, but no more promising from a business point of view than the myriad devices we'd been building or modifying for our medical customers during the previous eight years.

I didn't think I was doing anything out of the ordinary. Those lofty, idealistic notions of restoring life through electricity – sparked by the Frankenstein movies of my childhood – didn't enter my head, I'm quite certain, as I set about trying to solve Dr. Lillehei's problem.

Our first attempt to craft a more reliable (and portable) external pacemaker had us adding an automobile battery with an inverter to convert the six volts to 115 to run the AC pacemaker on its wheeled stand. That, however, seemed like an awfully inefficient way to do the job, since we needed only a 10-volt direct-current pulse to stimulate the heart. Transistors, which were then beginning to find wide application in electronics, seemed to offer a better solution.

Back at the garage, I dug out a back issue of *Popular Electronics* magazine in which I recalled seeing a circuit for an electronic, transistorized metronome. The circuit transmitted clicks through a loudspeaker; the rate of the clicks could be adjusted to fit the music. I simply modified that circuit and placed it, without the loudspeaker, in a four-inch-square, inch-and-a-half-thick metal box with terminals and switches on the outside – and that, as they say, was that. What we had was a small, self-contained, transistorized, battery-powered pacemaker that could be taped to the patient's chest or bed free of any cords and AC connections. The wires that carried the pulse to the heart could be passed through the patient's chest wall. When pacing was no longer needed, the wires could be carefully withdrawn without having to re-open the chest. Without any grandiose expectations for the device, I was moderately optimistic about what it might eventually do for Lillehei's patients. I drove the device over to the university's animal lab where it could be tested on a dog. Of course it worked.

The next day I returned to the hospital to work on another project when I happened to walk past a recovery room and spotted one of Lillehei's patients. I must have done a double-take when I glanced through the door. The little girl was wearing the prototype I had delivered only the day before! I was stunned. I quickly tracked down Lillehei and asked him what was going on. In his typically calm, measured, no-nonsense fashion, he explained that he'd been told by the lab the pacemaker worked, and he didn't want to waste another minute without it. He said he wouldn't allow a child to die because we hadn't used the best technology available.

So it was that after only four weeks of experimentation and work, the world's first wearable, battery-powered, transistorized cardiac pacemaker saw its first clinical application and began saving lives.

Nowadays, when it takes an average of seven years for a new medical device to find its way through the regulatory labyrinth in the United States, four weeks seems unbelievable. Just as improbable by today's standards is the idea that a manufacturer could take a new product from inception to operation in so short a period of time. But, in 1957, medical devices had not yet been placed under mandatory review by the U.S. Food and Drug Administration, so there were no regulatory hoops to jump through. At that point in our development, moreover, Medtronic was still a tiny shop, with scarcely a dozen employees and no bureaucracy. We constantly shared information and encouragement, but wasted little time debating whether we should build this or that product or enter such and such a business line. We were struggling to survive. When a customer asked for something, we provided it as quickly as we could – and only then hoped it might somehow earn us a few bucks. We were operating – not by design, but by necessity – according to a principle that has since been popularized by the statement *Ready, fire, aim!* We got the order, built the product, and only after rushing it to the customer debated its long-term possibilities for the company.

As it turned out, of course, that battery-powered pacemaker put us in the cardiac pacing business in a way that all of our earlier custom products had not put us in other businesses. That was in large part due to the response we received from Walt Lillehei's extensive and widely read writings about the device. Soon the general press picked up the story of the little metal box that kept children's hearts beating, and people were calling it a "miracle."

Within a relatively short time of its introduction, we were receiving orders from all over the country – from other countries as well. That did not mean, however, that Medtronic was all at once a dedicated pacemaker manufacturer. There weren't that many orders (about 60 by the end of 1958), and, besides, because this was truly a novel product designed for use in an area of medicine only then beginning to emerge, we had no idea of the size of the market. Pacemakers, for the time being at least, would be merely another item in our slowly growing, yet increasingly diverse, product line.

By the late '50s that line included AC defibrillators, insulated forceps, animal respirators, cardiac rate monitors, blood-gas shakers, physiologic stimulators, a bull-semen impedance meter, and now a cardiac pacemaker. We were, as an organization, still trying to discover who we might be when we grew up. We didn't even incorporate the company until 1957, the year we built that first pacemaker.

. . .

We didn't, for that matter, have time to brood on our eventual identity. The confluence of transistor, battery, materials, and cardiac-treatment technologies that helped make our first pacemaker a reality had created a fast-moving stream of new therapeutic possibilities.

In early 1959, for example, Dr. Samuel Hunter of St. Joseph's Hospital in St. Paul thought that our battery-powered pacemakers might be used to good effect on Stokes-Adams patients. (Stokes-Adams disease, usually affecting older patients, is a chronic, progressive condition that results in long-term heart block.) Hunter and a Medtronic engineer named Norman Roth proceeded to develop a new type of bipolar electrode that could be sutured to the patient's heart and more effectively concentrate the pacemaker's current where it was needed. The system required about 70 percent less current than existing electrode technology. The Hunter-Roth electrode was first implanted, in a 72-year-old Stokes-Adams patient, in the spring of 1959. The patient lived another seven years with the help of the device.

Yet, as promising as the new era of pacing therapy seemed at the time, there were some obvious and substantive drawbacks. Battery life of the external pacemaker was only about a month, so the power source had to be replaced frequently. And, despite its relatively small size, the unit was still awkward and inconvenient to wear, and made such everyday tasks as dressing and bathing difficult. In 1960, with these drawbacks in mind, we began working on implantable pacing devices.

We weren't the only ones. Indeed, the interest in new pacing technology had spread around the world, and doctors and engineers in several countries were all working on prototypes. Historians usually credit a Swedish team – Ake Senning, a surgeon, and Rune Elmqvist, an electrical engineer – with implanting the world's first internal pacemaker in 1958. That device, however, powered by a nickel-cadmium rechargeable battery, operated for only three hours. A second device, implanted in the same patient, lasted for a few weeks. (Interestingly enough, the patient, Arne Larsson, is still alive today, having had more than 25 different pacemakers during the past 41 years!) Meanwhile, in Buffalo, New York, Dr. William Chardack and Wilson Greatbatch, an engineer, began performing animal studies on the first implantable pacemaker powered by a primary battery developed in the United States. In early 1960, Chardack, his associate Dr. Andrew Gage, and Greatbatch implanted their device in a human patient for the first time, with encouraging results.

We got to know Chardack and Greatbatch after they expressed interest in the Hunter-Roth electrode that we were making by that time. We clearly had both scientific and commercial interests in common, so we decided to do business together. In October 1960, Palmer Hermundslie flew to Buffalo and signed a license agreement to use their names and patent, giving Medtronic the exclusive right to manufacture and market the Chardack-Greatbatch implantable pacemaker in exchange for 10-percent royalties on sales. By the end of the year, as we began production back in Minneapolis, Medtronic had 50 orders for the new device at $375 apiece.

Our formal relationship with Chardack and Greatbatch lasted for more than a decade. My fondness and admiration for the two men – bold and brilliant biomedical innovators both – continues to this day. My special affinity for Wilson Greatbatch owes a lot, no doubt, to the fact that we were both young electrical engineers with a deep and abiding interest in medical technology during those seminal times. Both of us had immersed ourselves in scientific journals since we were kids, yet we both were less interested in the theoretical aspects of electricity than its practical application, particularly in areas that could help keep people alive. The professional and eventually personal ties between us – like the ties that bound Walt Lillehei and his staff to Medtronic – would typify the relationships we have fostered over the years. I truly believe that those personal connections have been at least as important to our success as our products. To my eyes, high tech has always depended on high touch to be effective.

But I'm getting ahead of the story. By the end of 1960, Medtronic had become, by virtue of those budding relationships, a pioneer on the new frontier of implantable medical therapy. The fortuitous combination of technological progress, clinical experience, and social acceptance that was unavailable to earlier trailblazers like Lidwell and Hyman had created an unprecedented opportunity for our struggling little company. After nearly a dozen years and God knows how many starts and stops, we were finally on the brink of discovering our purpose in the brave new world of medical technology.

My parents, Florence and Osval Bakken. They established the values,
set the example, and provided me with the encouragement to explore the world around me.

Yours truly at about the age of one.
It wouldn't be long before an early fascination with
electricity would provoke my uncle to predict:
"That boy's going to electrocute himself someday."

Don't let the Sunday school suit fool you: At about the
time this photo was taken I was building cigarette-
smoking, knife-wielding robots in the basement.

My three years as an airborne-radar-
maintenance instructor in Florida during World
War II led me to a couple of important discoveries:
One, I liked to teach, and, two, I wanted to live
someday in a warm, sunny climate.

The new soldier poses with his new sister, Marjorie,
in front of their Columbia Heights home.

My mother is the center of attention when a grown-up
Marjorie, her husband Craig Andersen, my wife Connie, and
I get together circa early 1970s.

My four wonderful children with their
mother Connie and me in about 1970. From top
left to bottom: Jeff, Wendy, Brad, and Pam.

Years after this snapshot was taken, we honored this modest northeast Minneapolis structure as the birthplace of Medtronic. At the time, however, the crude boxcar-turned-garage-turned-repair shop was simply the best we could afford for our humble start-up operation.

I'm the young guy in the crewcut, hard at work in the president's suite at Medtronic's world headquarters, circa 1950. "Casual day" was still in the future. A flannel shirt and jeans was the uniform of the day, everyday, during our formative years.

My brother-in-law, co-founder, and partner Palmer Hermundslie and his beloved Beechcraft Bonanza, about 1960. A flyer during the war, Palmer went to great lengths to keep our young company airborne during its difficult first decade-and-a-half.

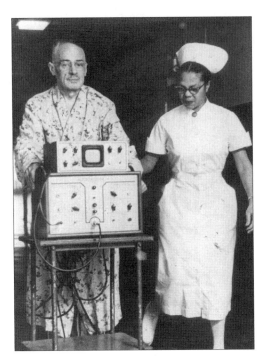

This big, bulky AC pacemaker was
state-of-the-art technology during the early 1950s.
Effective devices, especially in emergency
rooms, they were portable, however, in name only.
Their range was limited by the length of their
tether to the nearest electrical outlet.

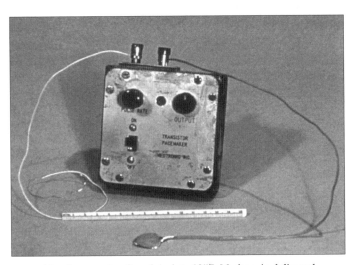

After four weeks of work in late 1957, Medtronic delivered
the world's first wearable, battery-powered, transistorized cardiac
pacemaker to surgeons at the University of Minnesota. Within hours,
the device was helping keep a pediatric heart patient alive.

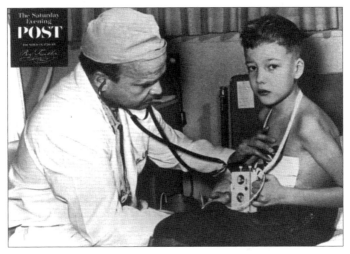

That first battery-powered wearable device put us in the pacing business in a big way. Our friend and collaborator, C. Walton Lillehei of the University of Minnesota, spread the word throughout the worldwide medical community. Then the press picked up the story. Soon the public was calling the technology a "miracle" that kept sick kids alive. In this famous photo from *The Saturday Evening Post,* Dr. Lillehei is shown with a young patient and an updated version of the original device.

Dr. Samuel Hunter (above) and Medtronic engineer Norman Roth developed a bipolar electrode that represented a major advance in pacing technology. First implanted in 1959, the Hunter-Roth lead helped contribute seven years of life to a 72-year-old Stokes-Adams disease patient in the Twin Cities.

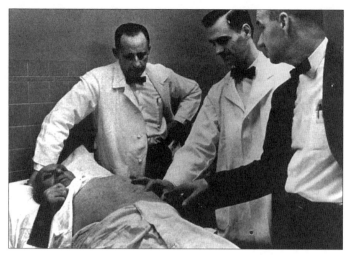

As surgeons and engineers around the world raced to
develop an effective implantable pacemaker, Dr. William Chardack and
Wilson Greatbatch, an electrical engineer, were making dramatic
progress in Buffalo, New York. In early 1960, Chardack and
his associate, Dr. Andrew Gage, successfully implanted their device in a
human for the first time. Later the same year Medtronic negotiated
the exclusive right to manufacture and market the Chardack-
Greatbatch implantable pacemaker. Here (left to right) Chardack,
Gage, and Greatbatch review their work.

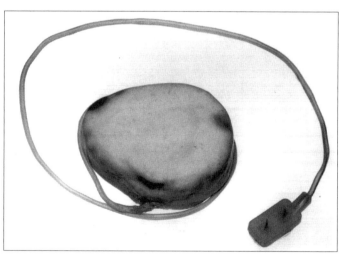

One of the first Chardack-Greatbatch
implantable pacemakers, with the Hunter-Roth electrode.

By 1959 Medtronic's family, while still small, had become a bit more "corporate" in appearance. That's me in the sports jacket on the far left and Palmer in the suit and tie on the far right.

In October 1968 we laid the cornerstone of a new St. Anthony addition
in the Twin Cities. As the literature in my left hand suggests, however, our sights
were even then trained on the future.

Medtronic was deep into the implantable-pacemaker
business when Palmer played tour guide to Minnesota Governor Elmer
L. Andersen (front, far left) and a delegation of state officials
and legislators during a visit to our St. Anthony plant.

Palmer's responsibilities ranged from sales and accounting
to personnel and construction. When he died, following a long illness,
in 1970, the company lost a co-founder whose leadership abilities
kept it going against all odds during the early years. I lost a
dear friend, mentor, and collaborator.

William Dietrich was so valuable a mentor and advisor during
Medtronic's early growth years that he was the one and only director
allowed to smoke a cigar during board meetings.

Wilson Greatbatch was not only a brilliant engineer and invaluable
collaborator, he became a close personal friend. Our common interest
in using electricity to help restore patients to health is but one
of the many affinities we've shared. I'm not sure when this photo of
the two of us chatting at Medtronic headquarters was taken.
Judging by the haircuts and lapel widths, I'd guess early 1970s.

I've been blessed over the years by the counsel and companionship of a series of wise and wonderful human beings. Here I am, circa 1970s, with one of the best and the brightest, Tom Holloran, a one-time Medtronic president and long-time member of the board.

Beginning in 1959, Medtronic's annual holiday program in December
has been an afternoon of fun, fellowship, and poignant reminders of our historic mission.
Important to the occasion as he is, even Santa has to take a back seat to the several
patients who, each year, tell our assembled employees how Medtronic devices have
restored them to full and productive lives. There's rarely a dry eye in the house.

Lyla Jane Koch received a Medtronic pacemaker when she was only a month old.
During a visit to Clearwater, Florida, in 1986, I had the opportunity to meet Lyla, who was
then a happy five-year-old. Now in her teens, Lyla is leading a healthy and happy life.

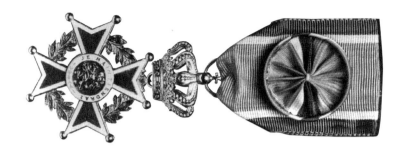

I was profoundly honored when her royal majesty, Queen Beatrix of The Netherlands, decorated me, in 1989, as an Officer in the Order of Oranje Nassau. The award, only rarely bestowed on foreigners, is given to persons who have made significant contributions to Dutch society.

On June 6, 1989, Minnesota Governor
Rudy Perpich honored me with a proclamation
acknowledging Medtronic's contributions to
biomedical technology in Minnesota and
throughout the world.

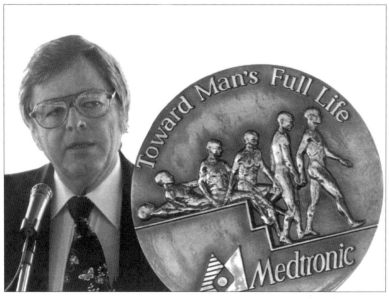

As part of its 25th anniversary celebration in 1974, the company
created the Medtronic medallion, which, as a silver-dollar-sized replica of the
display shown here, has been presented to every one of Medtronic's
20,000-plus employees the world over.

In March 1986 I was one of five recipients of the Centennial
Medal awarded by the College (now University) of St. Thomas in
St. Paul, Minnesota, for service to the state and mankind.

I was particularly pleased to receive an honorary doctor
of science degree from my alma mater, the University of Minnesota,
during the university's medical-school commencement in June 1988.
A month earlier, I had received an honorary doctor's degree
from Tulane University in New Orleans, during commencement
exercises at its school of engineering.

Since I abandoned the flannel shirt and blue jeans, my forays into the bolder designs of men's fashion have not gone unnoticed. This handsome sports coat, for example, never fails to elicit admiring smiles when I wear it during my annual holiday visit to corporate headquarters.

Our first battery-powered pacemaker relied on circuitry borrowed from plans for an electronic metronome. A metronome was thus an appropriate prop for this 40th-anniversary photo in 1989.

The Bakken Society, established in 1979,
honors Medtronic scientists and engineers who have made especially
significant contributions to the company's technology. This
photo was taken at the group's annual banquet in August 1998,
during which three new members were inaugurated.

Dale Olseth (shown here with me in the atrium
of Medtronic headquarters, about 1975) was first
a board member, then company president.
Dale's disciplined approach to leadership helped
bring our activities into tighter focus during the
late 1970s and early '80s.

The Bakken Library & Museum is recognized worldwide as a one-of-a-kind center for the study of electricity in medicine and life, drawing scholars, researchers, and students of all ages to its recently expanded facilities in south Minneapolis.

A community's vision realized. The North Hawaii Community Hospital, which opened in the spring of 1996, is a patient-centered facility. No where else has the most advanced diagnostic and therapeutic technology been integrated with millennia-old healing techniques in order to bring harmony to the health of mind, body, and spirit. High-tech and high-touch medical care have truly merged in one of the most beautiful natural settings in the world.

Winston Wallin, named our CEO in 1985, led Medtronic
to new heights by the early 1990s, directing a measured diversification
and helping the company regain its global pacing leadership.

Though officially retired from Medtronic, I remain closely associated
with the company, and at least three times a year visit corporate headquarters in the
Twin Cities. Here I join CEO William George alongside Paul Granlund's
"Life Center" sculpture outside Bill's office.

Doris and I on our wedding day – October 21, 1982 – during a
beautiful native ceremony in our adopted home on the Big Island of Hawaii.

Doris and I pose with a startling likeness of yours truly during
the bronze statue's dedication in front of Medtronic headquarters in
1995. My actual presence on the premises (about three times yearly)
has since been signaled by the appearance of one or more
Hawaiian leis around the statue's neck.

In June 1997 I was designated grand marshal of the annual
King Kamehameha Parade on the Big Island of Hawaii. Afterward,
Doris and I displayed our native finery for the camera.

One of my continuing non-business interests is the Pavek Museum of Broadcasting in St. Louis Park, Minnesota. There, students and hobbyists can find hundreds of radios and other equipment dating back to the earliest years of the broadcasting industry.

The rising figure symbolizes our mission to return men and women to full, productive lives.

During my long and instructive career in business, health care, and technology, I've come to believe that the "secret" to long-term success fits neatly on the face of a button. Pay special attention to the order of those three little words. It's READY, FIRE, AIM.

SIX

The Wide World of Medical Technology

By the end of 1959 – the end of our first full decade in business – Medtronic had become a global operation. The external pacemaker we developed for Walt Lillehei at the University of Minnesota two years earlier was in productive use throughout the world. Prominent American institutions such as the Mayo Clinic in Rochester, Minnesota; the National Institutes of Health in Bethesda, Maryland; and the Walter Reed Medical Center in Washington, D.C., were now among our customers, and so – almost miraculously, it seemed to us back at our modest headquarters in northeast Minneapolis – were a growing number of outstanding medical facilities in Canada, the Caribbean, Europe, South America, Africa, and Australia.

Our corporate numbers reflected the recent growth. Gross sales for the fiscal year 1959-'60 totaled $181,000, which was three times the comparable figure of five years earlier. More important, in the fiscal year that ended in 1960, sales from our own products – most prominently that external pacing device – accounted for over 60 percent of the total. We'd become, after a decade of dependence on other people's production, a full-fledged original equipment manufacturer in our own right. To the few dozen members of the Medtronic team at the time, that sense of development and contribution was rewarding indeed. Even more rewarding, when we paused for a moment to reflect on the matter, was the growing awareness that our hard work and inventiveness were actually helping physicians sustain and improve people's lives, which was my vision for electricity-based technology going back to that original *Frankenstein* film of my childhood.

As someone said of that point in our development, Medtronic's "garage era was over." That was literally, as well as figuratively, true. In 1959, we'd made plans to build a 15,000-square-foot office, lab, and manufacturing facility at 3055 Old Highway 8 in St. Anthony Village, a suburb on the north edge of Minneapolis, not far from our original site and the small apartment we'd rented to give us a little more room. The new building was financed through the sale of $215,000 of convertible debentures (which were shortly thereafter converted to common stock) and was ready for our use in the spring of 1961. At its "grand opening" in May, the contrast between our humble beginnings back there off Central Avenue and the new operation seemed almost comical. The new place even included a cafeteria, library, and auditorium – a far cry, to be sure, from the cramped work space and homemade desks of the garage! At the same time, it seemed inconceivable that we'd have to build two additions comprising 75,000 square feet before the end of the new decade, though that's exactly what we ended up doing.

To develop our overseas activity during that period, we contracted with a respected international distributor: Picker International Corporation, based in White Plains, New York. For about the next 10 years, Picker, with its more than 70 sales offices around the world, would be Medtronic's sole distributor outside the United States and Canada, and would help us truly realize our potential to be a leading player in the global marketplace. Here at home, Medtronic's sales network at the time comprised 14 representatives covering the U.S. and Canada, and five direct salespersons responsible for the Upper Midwest. We were still selling six other companies' product lines as well as our own, though our repping activity was making up less and less of our overall business.

Those long, full days of our early geographic expansion are wonderful to recall, though, like many events in our lives, they probably didn't seem so wonderful at the time. Palmer Hermundslie and I were on the road almost constantly, or so it seemed, calling on customers and working the trade shows. In Palmer's case, I should say "in the air" almost constantly. Palmer, you'll recall, was a dedicated and fearless pilot. Flying his snappy little Beechcraft Bonanza in and out of the Upper Midwest in all seasons and every sort of weather, he reported some harrowing experiences; having flown during the war, however, he was not to be fazed by something so trifling as a blizzard or thunderstorm. Despite (or maybe because of) my service with the Army Air Corps, I didn't like to fly, preferring to drive when it was practical or to take the train when it didn't make sense to drive.

In those days, of course, Medtronic was a newcomer on the national and international medical stage. Industry trade shows, for that matter, were not the elaborate, high-tech, multimedia events they are now. Basically, they were three- or four-day marathons during which you spent long, wearying hours standing in a cramped wooden booth you set up yourself in a stuffy corner of an auditorium, pressing the flesh, memorizing names and specialties, and explaining to whomever happened by who you were and what your products could do for their patients and institutions. Palmer or I would usually be the only Medtronic representative at the show, and when the show was over, it was up to us to take down the booth and pack up for the next stop.

(My early aversion to air travel would turn out to be not the least of the ironies of this story. I recently calculated that I've spent more than a year-and-a-half of my life in airplanes. I figured I've passed another four years working the trade-show circuit!)

What made that activity bearable – even wonderful in hindsight – was the opportunity travel afforded us to meet our customers face to face and learn directly from them what they needed and wanted from Medtronic. I'll talk more in Chapter Eight about the paramount importance of the customer; at this point, speaking about this stage in our company's development, suffice it to say that nothing we were doing back home in our lab and manufacturing space was more important than the relationships we were establishing on the road. We were learning that the key to success, by whatever means you wish to measure it, is not to build something and then hope someone will buy it, but to discover what the customer really needs and wants, then to meet or exceed the customer's expectations with both product and service. In many instances, the customer doesn't know what the product may be, unaware of the available (or oncoming) technology. He or she always knows, however, what wants and needs are going unmet, and this you most often learn one person at a time, face to face, asking questions and listening.

Driven primarily by customer demand during that period, our business continued to expand. In 1961 our proprietary line comprised 13 devices, including, besides the pacemaker, the Telecor heart-activity monitor with alarm and stimulator, and a coagulation generator that was used to control bleeding during surgery. A year later our line totaled 21 devices. Sales for the year that ended in April 1962 jumped over the $500,000 mark for the first time.

Not only was the "garage era" behind us, we were an international company with a growing product line, half way to our first million dollars. We were also – irony of ironies – drawing perilously close to insolvency.

. . .

Medtronic's financial data from that time revealed the bleak reality. The exhilarating growth that followed the development of, first, the external pacemaker and then its implantable successor was hugely expensive for a small, undercapitalized, relatively inexperienced company like ours. While our sales had climbed from $180,000 to more than $500,000 between fiscal '60 and '62, our losses rose like flood water, from $16,000 to $144,000. We'd been spending heavily – on research and development, improved facilities, expanded staff, trade-show presentations, cooperative ties with other research-oriented organizations, and other important components of the business – and, encouraging as they were, our sales had not kept up.

We'd borrowed more and more money in a vain attempt to keep pace. Now we discussed other possibilities: a public offering of Medtronic stock, private financing through a small business investment company, merging with another company in the field, even selling out to someone else.

At one point during this period, the Mallory company, whose batteries we were using in our pacemakers, offered to buy Medtronic. We had earlier issued debentures convertible to stock at $1.50 a share; Mallory offered to pay $3 a share for our stock. We were desperate enough, despite our growth and advances, to give the offer serious thought, figuring that if we did sell out, we'd at least get some money out of the crazy little business to which we'd devoted the last dozen years. Meanwhile, as we were thinking it over, Mallory was trying to determine the long-term prospects of cardiac pacing. Research that company had commissioned concluded that the all-time worldwide market for pacemakers would be 10,000 units. To us at the time, 10,000 units seemed an astronomical number. To Mallory, however, the game now didn't seem worth the candle. They promptly withdrew their offer.

Today, almost 40 years later, 10,000 is a tiny fraction of a worldwide market in which about 440,000 pacemakers are sold annually (about 115,000 in the United States alone). But what was small potatoes to a large company like Mallory proved to be a carrot to us. In fact, that figure, together with the enthusiasm and good wishes of our growing roster of customers, encouraged us to keep plugging along and, just as important, to concentrate our efforts in the pacing component of our business. Thankfully, in early 1962, we were able to secure long-term financing via a $100,000 note from Central Northwestern Bank and a private placement of $200,000 in convertible debentures with a local venture-capital firm called Community Investment Enterprises, Inc. That spring, we managed to record our first profitable month in more than two years.

Community Investment, I hasten to add, provided Medtronic with more than just a financial lifeboat. They supplied us with a handful of individuals who helped set our course and guided us through the shoals. Foremost among those individuals were William F. Dietrich, Community Investment's president, and Gerald W. Simonson, its vice president, both of whom joined our board of directors in the spring of 1962. That board included Palmer, me, and Thomas E. Holloran, a smart young Minneapolis attorney who served as our legal advisor and, soon, executive vice president. Within a year the board was further strengthened by the addition of Donald A. Shultheis, an officer of Northwestern Bank and later president of The Cambridge Corporation.

Though we didn't use the now-fashionable expression at the time, what we were undergoing was a dramatic transformation of our corporate culture. We'd been, from the beginning, a tightly knit group of engineers and technicians – plus one outstanding salesman – who operated pretty much by the seat of the pants. Ideas, innovations, and relationships had been more important than direction, oversight, and control. Bill Dietrich and the other newcomers were hard-nosed businessmen. They didn't understand as much as we did about electrical circuitry or the physiology of the heart, but they knew what made a business tick. Among other steps to protect their investment, they quickly instituted controls to keep track of every penny coming in and going out of the company, and even installed their own tough-minded comptroller to monitor the day-to-day spending.

More important, they insisted that we finally decide just what kind of company we wanted to be. Despite our pacemaker breakthrough, we were still all too willing to spend precious resources on other, often unrelated projects. Now, they said, we needed to take a good, hard look not only at the worldwide market for medical technology, but at ourselves. When we did the latter, we saw a company of about 50 hard-working employees. Half of those employees were engineers who, most of them anyway, could have made more money working for other, larger, better established companies in the Twin Cities. Most of those engineers were working for Medtronic because they believed they were doing something important with their lives. The pacemakers they were developing and building were helping make sick patients well.

It didn't take us long, then, to decide what we wanted to concentrate on as a company. We would dedicate ourselves to the development, manufacture, and sale of devices that restored people to meaningful lives. We would focus on implantable therapeutic technologies – as opposed to diagnostic or other laboratory products – and build the company around those technologies. Our written mission statement (which Dietrich et al. also insisted on) would reflect that decision. Though it took a great deal of time and discussion to agree on the right words, I believe that the statement very effectively summed up what Medtronic was at the time, is today, and will be – I hope and trust – well into the future. The first and foremost tenet of the statement (the complete text of which you'll find on page 124) reads:

"To contribute to human welfare by application of biomedical engineering in the research, design, manufacture, and sale of instruments or appliances that alleviate pain, restore health, and extend life."

An abbreviated version of that statement – *Toward Man's Full Life* – was adopted a few years later and inscribed on the medallion that we've presented to all Medtronic employees worldwide since our 25th anniversary in 1974. That medallion reminds us that our desire at Medtronic has never been to build cyborgs or six-million-dollar men or bionic women. Our desire from the beginning – codified during that stressful period in the early 1960s – has been and continues to be to restore "full life" to real people the world over.

Needless to say, we owe a great deal to the late Bill Dietrich, who remained a member of Medtronic's board until 1976, to Gerry Simonson, who's still a valued board member, and to Tom Holloran, who eventually served as president and also remains on the board, for not only helping us fix our course, but for finding the words to inspire and precisely describe it.

. . .

Our agreement on Medtronic's mission, as so stated, brought a new clarity to our professional activity. We began to phase out from our product line such diverse (and medically effective) devices as a varicose-vein eraser and a bladder stimulator in order to concentrate our efforts on implantable pacemakers and related technologies. At the same time, we began implementing business practices more in line with our mission, scope, and vision. We were transforming ourselves, in short, from an entrepreneurial start-up operation to a focused, growing, global corporation.

My transition from shirtsleeves entrepreneur to button-down chief executive – from product-focused engineer to company-oriented businessman – proceeded apace. Frankly, I'm not sure that I ever completely made the change. At any rate, I did my best to grow with the company – to learn the day-to-day mechanics of running a corporation and to find the right people to help me. If nothing else, moving from start-up operation to established business is a humbling process. Nobody, no matter what his or her background and skills, can do it alone. I've been blessed to have close at hand the likes of Tom Holloran, who, though not a technician himself, has had the judgment, integrity, and grace to be able to bridge the gap between the technical and business worlds. Tom is a careful man, but he was never one of those lawyers who tells you only what you can't do. Tom has been skilled enough to find the ways we can do the things we ought to do – very creatively, but always ethically and within the law. He has been, from the very beginning of our long relationship, a valued mentor and a great friend. Another invaluable mentor and friend, Bill Dietrich, taught all of us a great deal about the principles of running a successful business. (Bill was so important to Medtronic that he was the only person in the company's history allowed to puff on a cigar during a board meeting!)

Even with great help, though, the transition was a challenge. I don't know if anybody can help prepare a leader for laying off a significant portion of his company's workforce, as we were compelled to do to stay afloat in the early 1960s, or to wrestle with a major product failure, as we had to do during the middle '70s. Nothing, as far as that goes, can eliminate the pain that comes with the loss of a dear partner, or the loneliness and guilt a father feels as his children grow up while he's preoccupied with building his business.

Palmer Hermundslie died in 1970 after a long illness. He'd lived with adult diabetes since he was in the service, and in the past few years he'd been gradually losing his sight. In our transition from start-up to corporation he was no longer out selling, no longer flying his beloved Beechcraft to distant cities for trade shows and customer meetings, but he was still involved with the accounting and personnel functions of the business. He also played an essential role in our various building projects.

Looking back, it would be impossible to overestimate Palmer's contribution to the Medtronic story. More than anyone, he kept the operation on its feet in those early years when we were living hand-to-mouth. Out front, he taught us all the importance of the sale, that a business couldn't only build products, it had to sell them if it wanted to succeed. He also insisted that we build and operate the firm in accordance with the highest ethical standards, which we did. Behind the scenes, he would come up with the additional cash we'd need to get by during the leanest times. Though he frequently put his own money into the business, he was particularly effective in getting friends and acquaintances to invest in the company, even when it didn't seem like a very sound investment. As it turned out, of course, his powers of persuasion transformed a good many reluctant investors into enthusiastic millionaires. And those few individuals he didn't manage to convince would later wish they'd followed his advice. One fellow wanted to invest a thousand dollars with Palmer, but was dissuaded by his wife, who insisted they needed a better car more than some questionable Medtronic stock. Years later, the man would ruefully point to the automobile he bought with that money as his "$200,000 used car."

Palmer Hermundslie was a wise, generous, and honest man. When he died, he left a great many people a great deal richer than they were before they met him – and I mean richer in every sense of the word. His passing was an enormous loss for me, his family, his countless friends, and the company he helped found. In his honor we established a special meditation room bearing his name, first at our St. Anthony facility and then at our Corporate Center in Fridley – a reminder of his thoughtful approach to both business and life. I personally miss his companionship and counsel to this day.

As for my private life at the time, I can only reaffirm what many other business people have made achingly clear: that building a business and building a family are not readily compatible activities. Like most entrepreneurs and chief executives of growing companies, I would leave for the office early in the morning and return home late at night, often lugging a briefcase full of work home with me. I was frequently on the road for days at a time, and even weekends were consumed by company matters. It was hard on my family. Our two daughters and two sons – from oldest to youngest, Wendy, Jeff, Brad, and Pam – have grown up to be fine, upstanding, accomplished individuals, for which I give their mother Connie most of the credit, but my focus on the business cost us irreplaceable time together and led to Connie's and my divorce. Still, I'm not sure I could have done it any other way. Unfortunately, I don't think there's any alternative when starting and building a business than to give it everything you have, regardless of the personal sacrifice and disruption to the family. If you're not prepared for sacrifice and disruption, then you'd be well advised not to start a business.

In good times and bad, I should add, I was sustained by my faith in God and my association with the church I grew up in back in my old Columbia Heights neighborhood. Despite the other demands on my time, I always tried to be an active member of the First Lutheran Church, teaching Sunday school and serving for a while as president of the congregation. Even there, though, it was sometimes a challenge to stay the course. A pastor once wondered aloud if implanting electronic devices in human bodies – in God's temples – was morally defensible. I replied that God had given us the ability to develop such devices for the good of humankind and that our technology was helping restore patients' lives, surely a worthy activity in anybody's, even God's, eyes. And while I'm not sure I convinced the pastor entirely, he was certainly happy with the financial support we were able to provide the church because of Medtronic's success.

At the office, meanwhile, I discovered that I missed the hands-on activity – the day-to-day technical work, the engineering that brought me to the business in the first place – even more than I imagined. I was a kid, you will remember, who grew up monkeying with radios and building electrical robots; now, as CEO of a global corporation, I had by necessity abandoned the lab for the front office. It was a difficult transition, and it didn't happen overnight. Thankfully, I was able to make it, more or less. In fact – and more quickly than I might have expected – I learned to find great satisfaction in what others were doing at their workbenches, and to understand that what many of them had accomplished was far greater than anything I could have done myself.

My role, I decided, was to encourage our engineers in their activity, remind them of our corporate mission, help them see the big picture, and make sure they didn't limit their imaginations or stifle their creative urges. In later years I began using the phrase *Ready, fire, aim!* to help them break the bonds of excessive caution and crippling self-restraint when attempting to develop new technologies, to go with their hunches no matter how far-fetched or short of both planning and proof those hunches might be.

When I look back at all the wonderful products that have come out of our labs, I can only conclude that what Medtronic was able to encourage from its engineers and technicians has far exceeded anything I could have achieved on my own. And, all things considered, that has given me greater satisfaction than I ever could have imagined.

. . .

The 1960s, while personally challenging, were, corporately, the years when Medtronic came of age. Between fiscal 1962 and 1968, sales rose from $518,000 to almost $10 million. Net income leaped from nonexistent to a million dollars during the same period. Our "little family," meanwhile, grew almost tenfold – from fewer than 40 employees to nearly 350. The growth required two sizable additions to the St. Anthony facility. The additions included a state-of-the-art clean room for the assembly of our implantable products and more than double our operating space.

To better serve our overseas market, which now accounted for about a third of our total activity, we opened our first international facility – a service center at Schiphol Airport in Amsterdam, under the direction of an able young man by the name of Ron Hagenson – in 1967. (We had planned to establish our first international office in Tokyo, where we would study the Pacific market and introduce ourselves and our products to Japanese doctors. Then we decided that Europe was likely to be more important to us, at least in the near term, than the Far East, so we sent Ron to Holland instead. Ron's dedication and versatility, I might add, have stood him – and the company – in good stead, as he eventually became my right-hand man, and remains today, though in "semi-retirement," a close friend and advisor on a variety of important matters.) To keep us competitive with European-based manufacturers, we soon built our first overseas manufacturing plant, at Kerkrade, also in The Netherlands; production at the new Dutch facility began in early 1969. (Our Dutch ventures also brought to the fore a very capable young woman named Tinie Haagsma, who was our first European employee. Like Ron, Tinie played a long and highly valued role with the company, eventually coming to the United States and serving for 20 years as my personal secretary.) The following year, we broke ground for what would soon be our administrative, research, and manufacturing center, in the northern Twin Cities suburb of Fridley.

Though we were still manufacturing and selling a few other, noncardiac-related products, our growth was really fueled by the expanding acceptance of the implantable pacemaker. Several improvements had been made in pacing technology since we began manufacturing the Chardack-Greatbatch device in 1960. The most important of those, at least so far as early physician acceptance was concerned, was a safe and effective endocardial, or transvenous, pacemaker lead. Developed and improved by a series of brilliant physicians and scientists, the new lead allowed doctors to implant a pacemaker without a thoracotomy or general anesthesia. The body of the device, called the pulse generator, could be tucked just under the patient's skin; the wire lead from the pulse generator was then threaded through the subclavian, cephalic, or jugular vein to the heart. Medtronic introduced its Chardack endocardial lead system to an enthusiastic market in 1964.

The next major breakthrough was an implantable "demand-pacing" system that provided the electrical pulse when the heart needed the stimulus and then suppressed it when natural activity returned. Drawing once more on the research and innovations of many far-flung physicians and scientists, Medtronic released its first "demand" pacemakers in 1967. During the same period we bought all patents and patent applications relating to implantable pacemakers from William Chardack and Wilson Greatbatch, our friends and collaborators since 1960 – a step we believed put us in charge of our own destiny to a greater extent than ever before.

As I've said earlier, we owe a great debt to Chardack and Greatbatch – and not only for their technical achievements in pacing. In the early days of effective pacing, the public and the press saw us as white knights. Dramatic stories about the very visible results of pacing on patients ranging from "blue babies" to elderly heart-block sufferers were common in newspapers and magazines during the late 1950s and early '60s. Sure, there was resistance in some religious quarters, where it was felt that implanting a man-made device in another human being came too close to playing God, but such opposition was becoming rare. The tough nut to crack, ironically, was the medical profession itself. It was darned tough selling the implantable pacemaker to doctors early on. Doctors, in fact, would often avoid Palmer and me at trade shows and other gatherings. What we didn't grasp right away was that it took a doctor to sell doctors on the idea of implantable pacing, just as it had taken a doctor, Walt Lillehei, to spread the good news about the wearable external pacemaker a few years earlier. So our best sales tool when we first began producing the implantable devices were the talks and papers Dr. Chardack presented at surgical conferences around the world; slowly but surely he convinced his fellow physicians that pacing was an effective and worthwhile therapy. That taught us that the best way to promote a new device was not only face to face, but colleague to colleague – especially when the outcomes were so dramatic. Chardack led the way.

Even then, however, pacemaker sales, while growing steadily, were a long way from the levels we enjoy today. In the middle-1960s a pacemaker typically cost between $300 and $500, which was a lot of money to most patients in those days. Many individuals, in other words, who could have benefitted from pacing simply could not afford it. Indeed, it was not uncommon for communities and civic organizations to put on picnics and stage other fundraisers to help buy a pacemaker for a local patient.

The real breakthrough, as far as U.S. pacemaker sales were concerned, followed Congressional passage of Medicare legislation in 1965. Under Medicare provisions, the federal government would cover the cost of a pacemaker for qualified elderly patients, who, then as now, made up the largest portion of the pacing market. Because of Medicare, pacing technology was eventually available to virtually every U.S. patient who needed one. And because of Medicare, along with increasing physician acceptance, pacemaker sales (ours and our competitors') really began to take off in the late 1960s. Medicare reimbursement thus ranks with the development of open-heart surgery, the evolution of transistor and battery technology, and the emergence of new coatings and materials as essential elements that made implantable pacing a viable reality in our time.

. . .

In April 1974, Medtronic celebrated its 25th anniversary. For those of us present at or near the company's creation back in 1949, such a milestone scarcely seemed possible. A commemorative article written by our public relations staff at the time summed up the sense of unreality and wonder with these words:

"For a company that has established itself as a leader in the field of biomedical engineering, is the world's largest manufacturer of pacemakers, and will soon gross $100 million annually, Medtronic certainly had a modest beginning some 25 years ago."

At 25 years of age, Medtronic was marketing its products directly in more than 70 countries around the world. In addition to its U.S. and Dutch facilities, the company had opened manufacturing plants in Puerto Rico, Argentina, and Brazil. Our family of pacemakers comprised 14 implantable pulse generator models, four external pacing systems, and 10 different leads. In collaboration with Alcatel, a French power-source manufacturer, we had recently developed the world's first effective isotopic pacemaker. We had also introduced a sutureless myocardial lead, featuring a unique screw-in electrode for easier, safer, and more effective attachment to the heart. These and other advances during the previous few years permitted us to offer a line of pacing systems that were significantly longer-lived, more reliable, more simply and effectively implanted, and less expensive than their predecessors of only a few years earlier.

And, though our pacing business accounted for about 80 percent of our total sales at the time, we were aggressively researching and developing products for the neurological and rehabilitative markets as well. These included a dorsal-column stimulator, transcutaneous nerve stimulator, and a handful of other devices intended to help relieve pain and restore normal life. We were not a company to rest on our laurels. Not only was the market constantly changing, growing, and offering fresh opportunities; competition both in the United States and abroad was fierce, our customers were becoming more sophisticated and demanding, and government regulation was becoming a significant factor. Even more to the point, however, was the desire of our own people to keep extending the technological boundaries within which we worked.

One of our leading engineers, Bob Wingrove, for example, was talking and writing about a 10-year pacemaker long before there was such a thing. At the time, during the 1960s, pacemaker longevity was typically two or three years. But Bob knew we could do better. Through the use of microelectronics to reduce the current drain of the circuit, improved electrodes that would require less current to stimulate the heart, and the potential of a new power source, he believed a 10-year pacemaker was not only possible, but imminent. Bob was right. And he not only led us toward that longer-lived device, he was also a leader in the dramatic miniaturization of pacemakers and eventually into digital pacing systems. Many of us could see other later developments, too – programmable and rate-responsive pacemakers, for instance – that, after years of trial and error, research and experimentation, also became a reality.

When I think about those years so full of both problems and promise, I recall a dinner party back in about 1963. We were at long last beginning to make a little money and could see some hope of viability in the pacing business. During that dinner, one of our officers asked Bill Chardack what product he thought we should invest in next – that is, what product would be, in effect, the next pacemaker?

Chardack pondered the question for a moment, then said: "There will never be another pacemaker. Invest in real estate."

That proved to be good advice, at least for the gentleman who asked the question. He did invest in real estate, profited handsomely, and retired to the mountains at the age of 45.

Chardack was right about the pacemaker, too. There has never been anything quite like it in our industry – nothing that's achieved the clear and simple, black-and-white mass success in the marketplace that the pacemaker has enjoyed over the past 40 years. That pacing systems are still at the heart of our diversified business three decades later, that our state-of-the-art pacemakers are restoring millions of patients around the world to normal lives, tells me that those of us who stayed the course at Medtronic have invested wisely, too.

SEVEN

State of the Art

In the spring of 1989, on the occasion of the company's 40th anniversary, I was asked to compare "today's Medtronic" with the "early Medtronic." What did the two of them have in common?

On the face of it, I could have said, the "two" Medtronics shared very little. Entering our fifth decade in business, Medtronic was reporting sales of nearly three-quarters of a billion dollars, employed more than 6,300 men and women around the world, and marketed its products in 80 countries. Besides maintaining our role as the world's leading producer of pacing technology, we were a major manufacturer of prosthetic heart valves, membrane oxygenators, therapeutic catheters, nerve- and muscle-stimulation devices, drug-delivery systems, and other technologies that drew on the company's expertise in implantable and electrophysiologic therapies. Since 1977 our stock had been traded on the New York Stock Exchange, and, since 1985, we'd been listed among the Fortune 500 largest publicly held corporations in America. Quite a leap, I could have said, from the "garage era" when Palmer Hermundslie and I and a handful of other hearty souls were selling other companies' products and fixing broken television sets to make ends meet.

What I said, however, was that I didn't think the "old" and "new" Medtronics were fundamentally different at all. Though we didn't have a formal mission statement in the early days, we did try to operate according to certain principles. We wanted to do right by our customers. We believed in the importance of providing the highest quality products and service. We also viewed ourselves as a team, a family. I recalled being told that when we reached 100 employees, that sense of family would vanish. It didn't happen. Then I was warned that when we grew to be 250, we'd lose the family feeling. That didn't happen, either. Now, in 1989, with over

6,300 full-time employees, I said, we were still operating as a team and that the sense of family was very much alive and well among Medtronic employees around the world.

Happily, as we celebrate our 50th anniversary in 1999, I can respond to that question in pretty much the same terms, even with the subsequent explosion of the numbers. Though now a $4.0-billion corporation, with more than 20,000 employees in four diversified businesses, specializing in implantable and interventional therapies, we are a team – a family – committed to our historic mission, to doing right by our customers, to providing unsurpassed products and service that restore patients' lives.

Like most families, we've had our troubles as well as our triumphs. It is extraordinary enough for a technology company (for any company) to remain independent and in business for nearly half a century; to not have setbacks and disappointments would be unthinkable. But through both our ups and our downs, I'm convinced that Medtronic has prevailed because we've believed in ourselves working together for the greater good that is expressed in our mission statement. I'm pleased I can say the same thing today and looking ahead into the future.

. . .

Looking back, I wonder, as do most folks at a certain point in their lives, where the decades went, how they could fly by so swiftly. I see old, familiar faces – Walt Lillehei's, Gerry Simonson's, Sam Hunter's, and Tom Holloran's among them – and marvel that so many important events, featuring so many wonderful people, could so quickly fill a lifetime.

If the 1950s were our "garage era" and the '60s marked our passage from fledgling local enterprise to striving global corporation, the 1970s saw our emergence as a widespread medical-technology company operating in a brave new world of both promise and peril.

Medicare reimbursement in the United States, a growing acceptance of implantable therapies throughout the world, and continuing breakthroughs in science and technology had combined to create unprecedented opportunities for leading-edge manufacturers like Medtronic. And, indeed, a brief review of some of the milestones during the years surrounding our 25th anniversary in 1974 suggest what a rich period it was. The milestones include the establishment of our Micro-Rel subsidiary to produce hybrid electronic circuits for our implantable devices; the opening of manufacturing plants in Puerto Rico and Ontario, Canada, and a research center in Massachusetts; the beginning of direct operations in Japan; the production of long-lasting lithium batteries by our Promeon subsidiary; the introduction of our tined pacemaker lead; the implantation of our first PISCES spinal-cord stimulation device for treating chronic pain and of the first Medtronic Hall mechanical heart valve; the incorporation of the Medtronic Foundation to promote the company's growing philanthropic activities.

But the '70s were troubling times, too. In 1972, while manufacturers were competing to develop a longer-lasting pacemaker, four members of the Medtronic team left us to form their own company, Cardiac Pacemakers, Inc. (CPI), in St. Paul, and began producing pacing systems using the new, longer-lived lithium batteries. CPI was not the first, and would certainly not be the last, company to be formed by erstwhile Medtronic personnel; a recent review of our "family tree" identified more than 35 separate companies founded by former Medtronic employees – and there may well be more. But coming when it did and involving critical battery technology, CPI's creation was especially significant in competitive terms, as the newer company quickly grabbed 10 percent of the market. It was also, in a more personal sense, a considerable shock to our concept of family.

More traumatic yet was the problem we had with our Xytron pacemaker beginning in 1976. Body fluids had infiltrated the pulse generator in a small number of the units, causing the devices to short out. Despite the small sample, the problem was extensive because we couldn't be sure which units would exhibit the problem. Thus every one of our physician customers and every one of our Xytron patients, had to be informed. There's no evidence that anyone died as the result of the problem; still, the episode was extremely painful both to the company and to us as individuals. Confidence in our products and in our capability as a manufacturer was shaken. Our share of the worldwide pacing market, which had been up to about 65 percent during the early '70s, dropped like a rock, to less than 40 percent, by 1978.

As for me, I find it difficult to this day to express my disappointment. Xytron was our first system to employ integrated miniature circuits. We'd tested it extensively – though obviously not long enough. Following the failure, I was given the cold shoulder by many of our good customers – I was kicked out of some doctors' offices. Given the extreme importance I'd always placed on close personal relationships between Medtronic and the medical community, that anger and disappointment really hurt. It was impossible for me to not take it personally.

But you learn from your setbacks and failures – more from them, in fact, than from your successes. We brought on a large number of additional materials scientists to make sure the Xytron problem didn't happen again; and, in spite of the loss of confidence and customers, we forged ahead with new products. In fact, the Xytron issue unfortunately overshadowed some of the important advances our scientists and engineers were pushing through during the period. Among these were the Xyrel system, our first rate-programmable, lithium-powered, implantable pacemaker, introduced in 1977; the Spectrax SX, a multiprogrammable pacemaker that gave physicians the ability to adjust its function in response to a patient's changing requirements without additional surgery, implanted for the first time the following year; and the Byrel system, the first A-V sequential pacemaker, introduced in 1979. Each of these products, with their high degree of effectiveness and reliability, would contribute to the restoration of our status in the industry, as well as to our temporarily flagging sales.

Not surprisingly, the 1970s and early '80s required a series of self-examinations and adjustments at all levels of the company. Besides the competitive losses and product problem, our efforts were hampered, it had eventually become clear, by our old tendency to try to do too much with our available resources. Some people said we were straying too far from what we did best and that our movement back into diagnostic technologies, for example, had distracted us from our focus on therapies, hurting our product-development efforts as well as our bottom line. The times, as well as the situation, seemed to demand changes at the top. Tom Holloran, who succeeded me as president in 1967, turned the job over to Dale Olseth, another member of the board, in 1975, who was in turn succeeded by Winston Wallin, yet another board member, in 1985.

Chairman of the board for much of that time, I was also responsible for the company's research activities and various administrative functions. I could see that even with our mission statement in place, we simply weren't operating with as tight a focus as we should have. As a company, we were still inclined to jump at new opportunities so long as they seemed to offer some chance of growth; hence the large and potentially disastrous expenditures on the development and sale of monitoring and diagnostic products in the 1970s. Olseth, who came to us from the Tonka Corporation (he'd been a member of our board since 1973), brought a toughness and discipline to our operations, and Wallin, who came here from The Pillsbury Company (and who had been a Medtronic board member since 1978), finally put us on the path to a measured and effective diversification.

Through it all, our scientists and engineers continued to provide us with the technology not only to maintain our global presence in pacing products, but to retain our worldwide leadership. The Xytron failure proved to be a watershed for us in more ways than one. Doctors no longer felt that Medtronic could do no wrong; increasingly, they wanted to choose not only among different manufacturers' products, but among different models with different features. As a result, we were among the first manufacturers to get into what's now called "mass customization," which means that instead of selling a single pacing system for all needs and wants, you offer a line of different pulse generators with a line of different leads, so individual physicians can put together the specific systems they desire to meet their patients' needs. Such differentiation was a response to the widely varying practice styles apparent among doctors, as well as to the growing specialization among surgeons, cardiologists, and electrophysiologists taking place at the time. In 1981, the Medtronic Versatrax, the world's first dual-chamber pacemaker, was implanted, and, in 1983, the company introduced Itrel, its first fully implantable neurological stimulator. In 1984, doctors implanted for the first time our Activitrax system, the world's first rate-responsive single-chamber pacemaker. A truly groundbreaking, state-of-the-art device, Activitrax used sensors to monitor the physical activity of its wearer and thus adjusted the heart rate as needed.

By sheer but happy coincidence, 1984 was also the year the National Society of Professional Engineers named the cardiac pacemaker one of the 10 outstanding engineering achievements of the second half of the 20th century.

. . .

I had been continuing my personal transition during the period. There were times, to be sure, when I would have welcomed that tranquil corner of the isolated lab, where I could have labored over my schematics and circuit boards untroubled by the furor outside. But having "suddenly" (or so it seemed) reached my middle years – and having invested more than half of those years with my one and only business – I was reasonably comfortable in my leadership role.

That comfort hadn't come easily. I was, as I've said before, a shy fellow by nature. I had always enjoyed leading my friends in play and, later, my colleagues on the job, but, paradoxically, I suppose, I didn't like to call attention to myself or be at the center of a large crowd.

But serving as the chief executive of a major corporation simply required that I overcome my inhibitions and assume my position at the head of the table. With the help of my family and my staff, I took pains to look and sound more presidential. Accompanied by my wife Connie, I made several trips to Liemandts, a fashionable men's-wear shop in downtown Minneapolis, and exchanged my flannel shirts for three-piece suits. I also spent a great deal of time working on my public speaking skills. I had been out dealing with our customers on a one-to-one basis since 1949; now, with the growing interest in implantable therapies, it was necessary for me to address large conference rooms full of doctors, nurses, and administrators. In other words, there was more than my personal comfort at stake – the success of our business depended, at least to some degree, on my ability to communicate our message. To my considerable surprise, I discovered that I enjoyed speaking in public. I found myself energized by the opportunity to connect with big groups of influential people, to share my thoughts and ideas with them and to receive their feedback.

Working by myself in that isolated corner of the lab, I would likely have to wait years for meaningful response to my ideas – which, at an earlier stage of my life, would have been all right with me. As a young engineer, the thought of getting up and giving a talk or trying to motivate others was the farthest thing from my mind. Now, after several years of doing just that, I find it a tremendous thrill as well as a challenge to my leadership and communication skills. Not long ago I was asked to give the commencement address to graduating engineering students at my alma mater, the University of Minnesota. What in the world, I wondered, was I going to tell these young people? Until fairly close to commencement day, I still didn't know. But that uncertainty, followed by the development of a series of speaking points based on the *Ready, fire, aim!* theme, followed by the speech itself, was exciting for me – as was the spirited response I received from so many of those bright young engineers.

I had always enjoyed traveling, calling on customers, and showing the corporate flag at trade shows; my preferred conveyance, however, was my car or a train. Now I was learning to enjoy air travel. Of course, I had little choice. We were a global company, with important markets literally on the other side of the earth, so flight was the only practical means by which to meet and get to know our distant customers and employees.

Perhaps the most unexpected pleasure of my personal evolution, though, originated with an idea for the company's holiday party. After many years of picnics and dinners for company get-togethers, our Activities Committee, during the mid-1960s, suggested a holiday dinner and dance. Because I didn't dance, I didn't think much of the idea, but it was the committee's decision so I went along with it. In fact, in the spirit of the occasion, I went so far as to say, "Connie and I will be the first ones out on the floor!" It was one of those half-baked things you say sometimes, but my wife, if no one else, took it seriously. She signed us up for dance instruction, and over the next several weeks I learned how to dance. I should say, for accuracy's sake, I learned how to dance well enough to not make a fool of myself at that holiday party.

But, oddly enough, by then I was hooked on ballroom dancing. Connie and I continued to take lessons and really became serious about the activity. My commitment to corporate morale aside, I personally found dancing appealing because it's a very complicated endeavor, requiring a great deal of study and practice in order to excel. There's a certain mechanical component in learning the individual steps, as well as a definite emotional release in yielding to the feel and flow of the music. It was a wonderful experience! I had never had any association with music at all; now I was learning to understand and appreciate the rhythms of the waltz, the rhumba, and the cha-cha.

And, again to my surprise, I actually became fairly proficient at ballroom dancing. After about a year of lessons and steady practice, Connie and I passed our bronze-level test, then progressed to the silver and gold levels, finally even teaching at the bronze level as an after-hours activity. I still love to dance. I've never been a fisherman, golfer, or tennis player. Instead, I dance for exercise and pleasure. But while it's simply fun now, it was, for many years, a very welcome diversion from the intensity and pressures of the job.

. . .

Those pressures didn't ease appreciably, either, as we worked our way into the 1980s. We had fallen off the ambitious pace we set for ourselves a decade or so earlier, when we were growing at a steady 15-percent annual rate. When we were at about a couple of hundred million dollars in annual sales, we believed we'd crack the billion-dollar mark by 1988. After the Xytron failure and the flattened growth trajectory that followed, it was all too clear that we'd need a few more years to reach that level than we'd originally thought.

What some people described as the stagnation of our business in the late '70s and early '80s resulted, meanwhile, in a loss of confidence, of heart, among members of the Medtronic family. Morale in some parts of the company was uncharacteristically low. Those were trying times, it's true, but I was always positive and optimistic. I believed as much then as ever in our historic mission. I knew what our scientists and technicians and salespeople could do. I was convinced that if our company could build products that really helped people – that could extend and improve the quality of people's lives – it would "simply" be a matter of operating the business side right that would allow us to succeed.

When Win Wallin became our president and CEO in 1985, our share of the worldwide pacing market was slipping again. Many of our products were not perceived to be markedly superior to our competition's, and our attempts to expand into other therapies hadn't been sufficient to make us more than a basically one-product (pacemaker) operation. Win had not come out of a technology background (nor, for that matter, had either Holloran or Olseth, his predecessors); another Minneapolis native and University of Minnesota grad, he'd spent his entire career in the grain-milling and food business, most recently as chief operating officer at Pillsbury. But Win had been on our board for seven years when he took over as CEO, and he was a quick learner. He understood both the problems and the potential of the company. He wasted no time getting down to work.

He knew, for instance, that for Medtronic to regain its historic leadership of the pacing business, we had to have demonstrably superior products. (It was no longer enough to say Medtronic on the package.) Our first generation of Activitrax rate-responsive pacing systems, introduced commercially outside the United States in 1984 and launched commercially in the U.S. a year later, would give us a huge boost in the right direction, but a continual succession of smaller, more efficient pacemakers would have to follow. Thus Medtronic, in 1985, doubled its annual investment in research and development, bringing it up to nine and then 11 percent of net sales. The idea was to develop new technologies while ensuring a steady stream of enhancements within existing product lines.

The renewed emphasis on product development and improvement was readily apparent by the time our 40th anniversary rolled around in 1989. In our pacing business alone, new products included the Minix pacemaker, our smallest single-chamber device to date; Synergyst and Synergyst II, which combined our rate-responsive and dual-chamber pacing technologies; and the CapSure steroid-eluting pacing lead. The CapSure neatly represented the incremental enhancement of an existing product. The steroid it released kept the threshold level low enough to maintain pacing, requiring less power output from the pulse generator, and thus extending the working life of the entire system. In 1989, Medtronic held more than 40 percent of the unit share of the global pacing market, which was then estimated to comprise about

280,000 units and $1.2 billion in revenues. Through the introduction of new products like Synergyst and CapSure, we believed we could grow at a faster rate than the three to four percent pace of the market.

Equally noteworthy as Medtronic entered its fifth decade in business were the aggressive moves the company had taken to grow and diversify via acquisition. In the previous few years we had acquired high-quality pacemaker manufacturers based in Italy and The Netherlands; the cardiovascular division of the U.S.-based Johnson & Johnson company, whose assets included a line of tissue heart valves and a membrane oxygenator for open-heart surgery; leading manufacturers of coronary angioplasty catheters and guiding catheters; and a maker of TENS products. During the same period we released our advanced X-trel spinal-cord stimulation system for chronic pain, Thruflex catheter for coronary angioplasty, and SynchroMed implantable, programmable drug-delivery system that, remarkably, directs medication to a specific location in a patient's body at a prescribed and adjustable time, interval, and dosage. The company's 1989 annual report summed up our strategic position succinctly: "Through internal development and selective acquisition, the company is playing an increasingly significant role in five large and growing areas of therapeutic treatment...bradycardia pacing, tachyarrhythmia management, cardiovascular surgery, vascular therapy, and neurological stimulation. Medtronic's objective is to continue to diversify and grow, making the most of its pioneering technologies and rededicating itself to its long-standing mission."

That anniversary year's annual report noted two other important developments, one speaking to the company's future, the other providing a reminder of its past. The first was the naming of William George, formerly president of Honeywell's space and aviation systems business, as Medtronic president and chief operating officer. The second was the retirement of yours truly as senior chairman of the Medtronic board and a company officer. (I remained a member of the board until my 70th birthday in 1994.)

On a purely personal level, the two announcements were welcome indeed. Bill was clearly a highly intelligent, tough-minded, hard-working young executive who seemed an obvious choice to work with chairman and CEO Win Wallin and Dr. Glen Nelson, our board vice chair, leading the rejuvenated Medtronic to the end of this century and into the next. I was 65 years old in 1989. While I was excited by the company's prospects under its new leadership, I had other irons in the fire and was ready to move on. Besides, I was not really cutting my ties to the company. Win and, later, Bill were gracious enough to give me an open invitation to speak to the board whenever I wished; they would seek my input on any number of scientific and business issues, and encourage me to represent the company at scientific conferences and industry gatherings around the world. I would, in addition, retain my cherished responsibility to greet each new employee, present each with a Medtronic medallion, discuss Medtronic's history, and explain the Medtronic mission that links all of us, old and new, in a common cause.

For the first time in 40 years my destination most mornings would not be the converted garage off Central Avenue, the Old Highway 8 facility, or our ever-expanding "campus" on lovely Rice Creek in Fridley. The company would honor me with a life-size statue in the plaza fronting our world headquarters (a Hawaiian lei draped around the statue's neck whenever I was in town) and welcome me on the several occasions during the year when I would be back in the Twin Cities on personal or professional business.

As Medtronic moved on, in other words, I would be gone, but not quite forgotten.

· · ·

As I look back on the several years that have elapsed since my retirement, I can only marvel at the vision, wisdom, and skill of those who have carried on after me.

Win Wallin handed over the chief executive's job to Bill George in 1991, and stepped down as board chairman in 1996. Arthur Collins joined Bill and Glen Nelson in what's now called the Office of the Chief Executive. Bill is currently chairman and CEO, and Art is president and COO. The company hit the billion-dollar sales mark in 1991 (only three years later than we'd predicted, as it turned out!) and doubled that achievement only five years later. Earnings jumped during the same five-year span from $133 million to almost $438 million. As of the beginning of 1999, Medtronic was serving customers and patients in more than 120 countries, with more than 20,000 employees working on products and therapies in five primary areas: Cardiac Rhythm Management, Vascular, Cardiac Surgery, Neurological and Spinal, and External Defibrillation.

Reorganized for the new century, Medtronic's Cardiac Rhythm Management business now consists of the bradycardia and tachyarrhythmia management, heart failure, and atrial fibrillation businesses. Our Vascular business includes coronary vascular and peripheral vascular organizations. Cardiac Surgery comprises heart valves, perfusion systems, and cannulae platforms, while Neurological incorporates neurostimulation, drug delivery, neurosurgical and spinal and functional diagnostics businesses. We have also ventured into the external defibrillation market with the addition of Medtronic Physio-Control of Redmond, Washington, the world's leading developer of external defibrillator/monitor/pacemakers for both out-of-hospital and hospital care.

The Cardiac Rhythm Management business was still our largest activity, accounting for more than 65 percent of annual revenues. Our bradycardia pacing products (for slow or irregular heartbeats caused by human electrical-system problems) once again held about half of the global market, while the tachyarrhythmia management business, serving doctors treating patients with abnormally fast heart rhythms, held about half of its market. At the same time, the bold but focused diversification activity of the previous decade had clearly made a difference. Our Neurological business itself was poised to be a billion-dollar enterprise in its own right in the near future.

The extraordinary numbers aside, I am most gratified that Medtronic continues to be true to its mission. It is, in its own words now, committed to "restoring lives through medical innovation" and envisioning itself as "the world's leading medical technology company specializing in implantable and interventional therapies." Its strategy is based on four sturdy legs: To grow market share in its core businesses, to meet unmet medical needs by leveraging its technology, to expand globally in both established and developing markets, and to acquire related businesses and technologies and thus establish new platforms for growth.

Medtronic's commitment to both its world and its own employees has been often honored – most recently by a pair of coveted awards given the company in just the past year. *Business Ethics* magazine honored Medtronic with its annual Award for General Excellence in Ethics, emphasizing the company's determination to be "the unsurpassed standard of comparison and to be recognized as a company of dedication, honesty, integrity, and service." "Medtronic's entire culture revolves around upholding those principles," the magazine wrote in its November/December 1997 issue. "[T]o portray Medtronic as just another highly profitable health-care company doesn't do it justice. At the heart of its success is an unwavering devotion to the highest possible legal, moral, and ethical standards...." Added Dr. Kenneth Goodpaster, a professor of business ethics at the University of St. Thomas in Minneapolis, "I'm impressed with their efforts to maintain their mission and vision in a highly quantified environment." Meanwhile, in its January 12, 1998, issue, no less than *Fortune* magazine named Medtronic one of "the 100 best companies to work for in America." In its citation, the publication mentioned the company's presentation to each new employee of the Medtronic medallion and mission statement and the annual holiday program at which employees have the opportunity to hear patients speak first-hand about the company's products. Needless to say, like every other member of the Medtronic family past and present, I'm extremely proud of both awards.

To this day, when I visit one of Medtronic's many facilities around the world and talk with its leadership, employees, and customers, I'm pleased to find that its commitment is, in fact, more than just the company line – that it is a deeply imbedded and, I hope, permanent part of the corporate culture. Nothing I can say about Medtronic today makes me happier or more optimistic about the future.

For these are not easy times in which to do business, and they're not going to get easier. The fast-rising cost of health care and the phenomenal growth of managed-care plans have made it essential for medical products to be provably cost-effective. We operate, moreover, in an environment of seemingly insatiable litigiousness and regulatory control unimagined when Palmer and I started the company – unimagined, for that matter, even a quarter of a century ago. In 1957, we moved that first battery-powered external pacemaker from concept to patient in four weeks; today, owing primarily to the regulatory hurdles a manufacturer must now negotiate in the United States, more than seven years is required on average for a new medical-technology product to reach the market! Small wonder that U.S. companies, including Medtronic, are doing more and more research and development abroad.

What concerns me from a technological point of view is the possibility that Medtronic will become too cautious and move too slowly to get therapies to the people who need them. I worry that we could spend so much time and effort getting ready and then aiming that we never get around to actually firing – or that when we do finally fire, the target has been struck by somebody else or has moved out of our range. If we're to stand by our commitment and maintain our competitive edge in this fast-paced world, we must ready ourselves and fire as quickly as we can – and then make the necessary adjustments. I am utterly convinced that this is the surest recipe for meaningful innovation. I'm equally convinced that our scientists and engineers are up to the task. (The best and the brightest of our creative, innovative people are annually honored in their own right by nomination and admission to the Bakken Society, which, since its creation in 1979, has cited almost 40 men and women who have made especially important contributions to the company's scientific and technological progress.)

There's been a lot of talk in recent years about "reinventing" corporations to meet the demands of the changing global marketplace. Medtronic, for its part, can certainly grow dramatically, even double its size, within the next few years by doing what it's doing so well right now: capturing more market share, finding new uses for its existing technologies, and developing or acquiring new products within its businesses. Meanwhile, reinventing the company means taking a good look at how we've evolved over the past 50 years, and determining which of the positive components of that growth will be applicable to our world tomorrow.

We must continue to stimulate and nurture the creative power of our 20,000-plus dedicated employees. We need to keep streamlining our infrastructure, to allow our creativity to manifest itself in new processes, products, and services. We have to move fast and efficiently, and not let cost controls, regulatory agencies, or the fear of lawsuits slow us down.

No, it won't be easy. But then, if history has taught us anything, it never is.

EIGHT

Aspects of Leadership

To live is to learn, someone once said. A corollary to that truism might be: To found and run a business is to learn the hard way.

Over the past half-century, I have learned a great deal about both business and life through my close and abiding relationship with Medtronic and the medical-technology industry. Much of what I've learned has come the hard way – through trial and error, via setback and disappointment, at least as much as from success. But that's the way – the hard way – I believe we learn best. The lessons that emerge from struggle, even abject failure, are the ones, in my experience, that tend to stick.

Upon my retirement as an officer of Medtronic in 1989, I thought long and hard about some of the most important lessons I had learned through the good times and bad that marked the company's first 40 years. The conclusions that resulted were gathered in a small collection of essays we called "Reflections on Leadership." Somewhat to my surprise, those "Reflections" were widely read, passed around, and commented on, both within the Medtronic organization and in wider business, medical, and academic circles outside. I was both flattered by the attention and heartened that my experience was presumably helpful to others. I was especially pleased that many young people – some of them fledgling engineers with an eye on starting their own technology company someday – seemed to find value in the lessons that I'd learned.

What I wrote then spoke of and to the Medtronic experience in particular, but the responses I've received suggest that the lessons might be universal. Thus, with the hope that what I learned will be as useful to others and their businesses as to the Medtronic family for which they were originally intended, I offer, in somewhat abbreviated form, a few of those reflections right here.

. . .

Nothing is more important to any company than its customer. He or she is more important than management meetings, planning sessions, or anything else we do in the name of the firm. Our customers must always come first.

For the company's representatives in the field, "customer first" is more than a strategy or slogan. It's the First Commandment, the basic law by which they conduct their professional lives. They see or talk with the customer every day of the week. They often go to extraordinary lengths to make sure the customer is satisfied. Medtronic's representatives have been known to drive hundreds of miles in the middle of the night to deliver a pacemaker to a physician. They have gone so far as to arrange the delivery of a competitor's device to a doctor who needed it when one of our own wasn't available. Medtronic's field representatives, I am very proud to say, have demonstrated time and again that they will meet the customer's needs regardless of the cost or the effort.

The same might be said of the company's engineers, its support staffs, receptionists, and other employees. In the design and manufacture of Medtronic products, in its marketing and advertising, in every one of its employees' diverse activities, the prevailing commandment is, or should be, "customer first."

Every customer of every company is important. I believe, however, that the customers of a medical-technology company must be treated with special care. They tend to be men and women of great intellect and education. Their technical expertise and experience is often staggering – as is their responsibility to their patients, whose lives may rest, quite literally, in their capable hands. Their time is precious, their patience sometimes short. Independent and proud, they do not appreciate being abandoned, slighted, or put on hold.

I believe, therefore, that the leaders of a medical-technology company must always be responsive to those customers' questions and desires. We must always take the time to meet with them, one on one, and listen to their thoughts about our common concerns. Medtronic was founded on responsiveness to its medical customers. It has grown and prospered because it has responded not only to what those customers need, but also to what they want. Medtronic will continue to grow and prosper, I'm convinced, as long as it listens and responds.

I have always been intrigued and enlightened by what I hear when I visit one of our customers in his or her office, lab, or operating room. A physician may be quite pleased with both our product and our local sales representative, yet harbor some negative feelings about the company. When questioned further, he or she may say that someone back in the Twin Cities has been short or abrasive on a billing matter, or has not responded promptly to a product-related query. Maybe the doctor has called our corporate headquarters wishing to speak to a particular officer, but was told that officer couldn't be disturbed. Such is not the kind of news we like to hear from customers, but it is news we must hear nonetheless.

In those settings, on the customer's turf, we can also learn what interests the physician both as a professional and as a human being. We can learn what the physician wants in the way of features, in addition to what he or she needs. Those wants may have little to do with the way a product actually functions, but they may make the doctor's efforts more efficient or less stressful. In any case, we may discover that if we don't furnish what that physician wants, another company will – and we'll have lost a customer.

For many years I've carried a pack of three-by-five cards on which I've recorded the wants and needs of our customers. I've also used the cards to record more personal information about customers' families, hobbies, special interests and concerns. The information from those cards is eventually filed in my computer, so the next time I meet with a customer, I can speak on a personal as well as professional level. The file also provides an up-to-date list to which I can mail both professional information and personal greetings a couple of times a year.

The larger a company becomes, of course, the greater the chance that its customers will perceive it as an unresponsive monolith whose leaders are far removed from their clinical concerns, not to mention their more personal interests. That perception is reinforced when the customer calls and can get only as far as an officer's voice mail. The customer may well be aware of the company's high-tech capabilities, yet at that moment wish for a more high-touch response.

A company's leadership, every bit as much as its most distant field representative, must allow themselves to touch and be touched by their customers. Those leaders must personally get out of the office, attend conventions and conferences, make calls with their sales people, and visit their customers. They must systematically and aggressively seek out, listen to, and respond to their customers' feelings about products, personnel, and procedures.

When a company's leaders make themselves available to their customers, they set a powerful example for everyone who works there. They are saying, with their actions as well as their words, that at their company the customer does indeed come first.

. . .

The jobs and responsibilities that make up a large corporation are many and diverse. Each of us is a specialist, with specific functions and assignments that may sometimes seem to have little direct connection to the functions and assignments of our colleagues. Yet, in even the largest organization, each of us has one imperative in common: our most important task is to help make the sale.

The sale. As one of my colleagues liked to put it, "That's the event." Everything else we do is either preliminary or after-the-fact. Nothing really happens until the sale is made. The company has nothing to show for the brilliance of its product until the product passes into the customer's hands. Only then does the company earn its appropriate reward in the way of revenue, growth, and the satisfaction of mission accomplished. Only then does it receive the means by which to continue to develop and market new products.

When a company is starting out, there is no doubt about the importance of the sale. Everybody knows the product, the demands of the market, and the customer. Everybody knows that livelihoods depend on bringing all the elements together to consummate the sale. Everybody eats, sleeps, and breathes the sale. They have to when they're small, or they simply won't survive.

When a company grows larger and more compartmentalized, that basic rule of survival is easy to be misplaced or overlooked. The director of sales isn't about to forget it, nor are any of the sales personnel out in the field. But what about the company's officers, with their various managerial responsibilities? What about the engineers in the company's laboratories, or the communications staff, secretaries, security personnel, and receptionists, with their precise job descriptions? What do they have to do with making the sale?

The answer, of course, is everything.

Everyone is in a position to help make the sale. By virtue of a pleasant, courteous, and sensitive manner, each of us, our official function notwithstanding, can leave a customer with a positive impression of the company and help ensure a continuing relationship. The tone of our correspondence, the way our telephone calls are answered, the friendliness of our co-workers, the appearance of our facilities – all of those factors and more contribute to the intangible yet vital impression that ultimately results in a sale. All of us must continually ask ourselves: How can I do my job so that it helps achieve the sale?

A top-to-bottom, companywide sales sensibility must be part of an organization's culture – just as it was when the organization was starting up. It must be an integral part of a company's mentality, like an ongoing commitment to quality. New employees must be instilled with this sensibility, veteran employees regularly reminded of it. A determination to contribute to the sale must be in the air the company breathes.

This is another way of saying that the customer comes first. No matter how large or diverse and successful our company becomes, we must keep in mind the company's absolute dependence on the person who purchases our products. No matter how ingeniously we plan, regardless of how energetically we develop our strategy, if we lose that customer, we don't make the sale, and if we don't make the sale we lose our hard-earned place in the sun.

. . .

One of the knottiest problems the leadership of any organization can face is the noisy, disruptive presence of a brilliant maverick. Aloof or contentious, he or she is the misfit, the troublemaker, the person with whom nobody, it seems, can get along, much less work productively. If that person were only cantankerous or uncooperative, leadership could simply show him or her the door. The problem arises when that maverick also happens to be a significant creative force, maybe even a genius.

Most good-sized companies have one or more such employees: dazzling inventors, gifted scientists or scholars who can see farther than their colleagues – farther, for that matter, than their leaders. These gifted individuals are impatient with their "slower," shorter-sighted co-workers, frustrated with their working procedures, and enraged by the limitations imposed on them by organizational structures and budgets. Prone to criticize and demean other employees, and often eager to defy their bosses, they break the rules with maddening frequency.

How should leaders deal with such individuals? The obvious solution is to fire them. Or to freeze them out. When they open their mouths, don't listen. When they submit ideas, file their memos in a drawer. Deal with these mavericks the way you might deal with unruly children. When they throw a tantrum, smile and walk away. Pray that one day they will grow up and either become congenial members of the corporate family or move out.

I don't think, though, that this is the proper response. As a matter of fact, I would view the isolation or departure of talented troublemakers not as the failure of the troublemakers themselves, but as a failure of leadership.

The reason is simple. That maverick may be the one person who can put the enterprise ahead of the competition – ahead, perhaps, by light years. Abrasive and obnoxious as mavericks can be, they may also be a decade or more ahead of their time. They may be thinking in revolutionary terms. They may have their eyes on a glowing light in the murky distance that, for the time being, only they can see.

Much of Medtronic's success has been the result of brilliant mavericks. We can look back, for instance, to William Chardack and Wilson Greatbatch, who helped us make the implantable pacemaker a worldwide success. Bill Chardack was especially difficult for our engineers to work with, disparaging nearly all of them at one time or another as incompetents. Greatbatch was a little smoother, but he was very technologically advanced and hard to get close to on a personal basis. Both were very determined, very demanding, very goal-oriented individuals. Both were also brilliant, and, difficult as it often was, we did our best to follow their suggestions and advice. And, thanks to their lead, we effected those early implantable-pacing breakthroughs.

There have been many mavericks at Medtronic. Some of them have been impossible for us to accommodate, and, sad to say, were encouraged or allowed to go their separate ways. Others have been effectively integrated into the Medtronic family, where they have been highly creative, albeit prickly, contributors. In demonstrating both patience and creativity when dealing with the latter, their managers have also demonstrated considerable leadership skills.

Those managers, first of all, have established and maintained an atmosphere in which new ideas can be easily heard and properly examined. Some have employed brainstorming sessions to encourage a free exchange of new ideas; some have set up special award systems in which fresh concepts are acknowledged and rewarded. Our better managers have found ways to pay attention to what their "idea people" are saying. In a word, they listen. They listen even when the listening isn't particularly easy or pleasant. They understand, as they listen, that their gifted mavericks do not always communicate in a direct or linear manner. The conversation jumps and darts and careens about the subject without the help of such niceties as background and transition. In some cases, the communication is both brilliant and unintelligible, and it's the job of the manager to provide for the essential interpretation or translation.

Mavericks sometimes demand their own company or department, where they can be their own boss and do their own thing. Unfortunately, at least in my experience, they are rarely effective managers. They have a tough time delegating authority, and, ironically enough, they're often not open to other people's ideas. Besides, they are usually not oriented to the bottom line. Their eyes are scanning the far horizon; they're simply too farsighted to see very clearly the problems immediately at hand.

Effective leadership neither buries brilliant mavericks nor lets them venture too far off on their own. With an enormous amount of imagination and patience, the most effective leaders accommodate their ornery thinkers and give them the attentive ear their ideas deserve. The challenge to leadership is great, but so, too, are the potential rewards. Indeed, as we at Medtronic have learned very well, the rewards can make a successful company.

. . .

It seems appropriate, when talking about creativity and innovation, to interrupt myself and include at this point some thoughts I jotted down way back in October 1979. What I had determined to do, on Medtronic's behalf, was isolate and identify what I labeled

115

"The Characteristics of a Technological Winner" – specifically, a "successful medical device."

My notes comprised five categories and several "characteristics," as well as a series of questions to ask about a new device. I believe those notes and questions are as pertinent today as they were when I wrote them.

Creators of a "technological winner" want to help someone, not simply produce a commercial success. They are usually medical personnel or engineers, often a medical professional with a technical orientation. If the creators are part of a team or organization, the team or organization tends to be small. In general, technological-winner creators do a lot of reading, writing, and talking to others in the medical and technology fields. They also exhibit a strong missionary zeal for their idea, displaying great persistence and powers of persuasion or coercion – often in the teeth of challenge and criticism – in order to see their idea accepted.

The environment or circumstance in which such winners are developed usually includes a medical setting (hospital or clinic) or a small organization. Development takes place in an atmosphere of freedom and openness, usually without government funding, and often as a byproduct of original research. Other, co-existent technological development has provided a "fit" for the new products. More often than not, the results of the development are never certain until the project is complete.

A winner's technology is usually simple in terms of the "state of the art" at the time. Recent technology is often applied to make an existing, or even old, idea clinically practical.

The devices themselves significantly help a patient in a way the patient could not otherwise be helped. The results are clear and demonstrable, restoring the patient as nearly as possible to original physiologic functions. The devices are usually worn by or implanted in the patient. The ideas behind the devices are not always obvious; in fact, they have at one time or another been denounced as blasphemy or quackery, though they are now socially acceptable. They are also cost-effective within the health-care system.

There is often no obvious market when the device is originally developed. But if a new device helps one patient, a market usually follows. Though it often takes time for a market to grow, the timing is right for the device's acceptance.

In sum, among the essential questions to ask about a new medical device are the following:

Does the device (or idea behind such a device) significantly and obviously help a patient return to full life?

Is it cost-effective?

Does it restore normal physiologic function?

Does it do something that can't be done by any other therapy? Is it by far the best solution to the problem?

Are the necessary complementary technologies in place?

Is there a close doctor-engineer relationship behind the device or idea?

Does it have a devoted "missionary" willing to promote it for a period of several years, against all criticism and ridicule?

If you can answer "Yes" to most, if not all, of those questions, you may well have a technological winner.

. . .

Before we built our own house on the Big Island of Hawaii, Doris and I loved to stay nearby at the Kona Village resort. Among the resort's many glorious attractions in my eyes was its policies and procedures – or, rather, the lack of same. In fact, if Kona Village has an official policy manual at all, I suspect it's an awfully slim volume. The few policies the resort does maintain seem to run along the lines of their "official dress code" for dinner: "No coat or tie."

My feelings toward official policies have hardly been a secret at Medtronic. There are, of course, significant differences between an island resort and a large technology company. Yet I believe that on the issue of official or institutional policies and procedures, the large company can learn something from the resort's example, which can be summed up by the axiom, *The fewer, the better.*

We severely limit ourselves, both as a company and as individuals within that company, with the dead weight of excessive policy, red tape, and bureaucracy. By any name, those policies that inhibit our flexibility and freedom of movement also tend to limit our personal and corporate growth. They stifle our creativity in research and development, interfere with our quest for quality and innovation in production, and work against our most imaginative efforts in marketing and sales.

Certainly organizations of all kinds and sizes must have some policies and operational procedures, lest they wander off into anarchy and chaos. At their best, institutional rules provide the guidelines by which a company conducts its business, both within and without its walls. Procedurally, they help define the form and the function of a company's divisions, and spare workers the need to re-invent the wheel for every new task. Too often, however, organizations add rules and regulations on top of those that are essential to doing business. They adopt new policies without winnowing out the old.

Policy gridlock and procedural overkill can be especially prevalent, it seems to me, in large, long-established companies. As they have grown and diversified over the decades, the number of rules and regulations have increased exponentially, until their policy manuals bulge with miscellany and junk like Fibber McGee's closet. A policy that made good sense 20 years ago may lack meaning and applicability today – yet no one has bothered to get rid of it. Small wonder that younger, smaller companies are often able to move faster and more efficiently. They are generally not as weighted down by the ball and chain of internal policy and procedure as their larger competitors.

Large companies, in order to compete with the upstarts, need to whittle away their obsolete and counterproductive policies, and keep only those that are essential to getting the job done right. Key leaders need to review their policies and procedures, and ask themselves, "Now how does this particular policy pertain to the sale? How does it relate to our technological progress? What effect does it have on product innovation and employee morale? Does this policy or procedure interfere with satisfying our customers' desires?"

I believe that the customers of a medical-technology company like Medtronic require special consideration in this regard. Physicians have so many frustrations in their professional activities that they're just not willing to go through an awful lot of effort to deal with a company that adds to those frustrations. If a device manufacturer, because of official policy or procedure, gives physicians a bad time on a credit matter or provides poor service with a product, they're simply going to buy from someone else. The manufacturer not only needs to offer them the most innovative and reliable products on the market, the company also has to make it as easy as possible to do business. The company can do that by cutting out unnecessary policies and procedures.

At the same time, manufacturers need to streamline their policies and procedures so the creativity of their employees is never discouraged. One of the saddest lines a technology company leader can hear is the complaint, "We spend 10 percent of our time coming up with new ideas – and 90 percent trying to work those ideas through the system." By stripping away the policy cobwebs that impede innovation, companies can give their creative people not only the freedom to develop fresh ideas, but the ability to see those ideas to fruition.

At island resorts, a bare minimum of restrictive policies results in greatly enhanced leisure-time pleasure. At global technology companies, a streamlined policy manual encourages creative people to make the most of their on-the-job opportunities and thus better serve the customer.

. . .

Is there a difference between leadership and management? Or are we merely playing word games? Are we talking substance here, or semantics?

I believe there is a difference, and that the difference is both meaningful and important. Leadership emphasizes (among other qualities) vision, experience, trust, communication, and self-confidence. Leadership is the state to which management should aspire.

Time was when all of us in positions of authority in a company or organization were managers. In the Industrial Age we managed both people and data, the former receiving only as much of the latter as we deemed necessary for them to do their jobs. Both our people and our data were eminently manageable – our people uneducated and dependent on us for their livelihoods, our data reaching us in easily consumed portions. Management meant the control of employees and information.

We live now, however, in an age of rapidly expanding information. Most of our employees are well-educated and well-informed. Their knowledge has freed them of the traditional dependence on their employer. The extraordinary deluge of data, meanwhile, has become more than we in the corporate or organizational hierarchy can control, much less master. Today we must share. Today we must lead.

Leaders have always distinguished themselves by the length and breadth of their vision. They see farther than their contemporaries, in large part because they're looking farther down the road. Managers tend to focus tightly on the here and now, their vision often not extending much beyond the next quarter. Leaders take the longer view necessary to chart the organization's growth five, 10, or even 20 years in the future.

Leaders, moreover, don't restrict their vision to a particular field. They understand that technology, for instance, is not isolated, but exists in a larger, ever-expanding context. They are aware of the growing impact on their environment of politics, economics, and demographic changes the world over. They know that a trend toward more stringent regulation in a European country and the aging population of an Asian nation can have a great deal to do with business here at home – if not immediately, then within the next several years.

To keep up with the data on such diverse subjects, leaders must read (or view: television and video cassettes offer an increasing number of educational opportunities) thoroughly and eclectically. They must also rely on their staffs for information-gathering and sharing purposes. They should understand that their employees have access to much of the same information that they have; the Information Age allows few secrets. Leaders must thus be consistently open and candid with their employees, while finding ways to help employees make the most of their own data flow.

Experience, of course, is the greatest teacher of all. Effective leaders are almost always well-traveled "explorers" who by virtue of their journeys and adventures can weigh hypothesis against actuality, theory against real life. In the area of medical technology, they know what the health-care professionals want, not only need, because they have met with those professionals in their hospitals, clinics, and labs. They know, as well, what the international scientific community is thinking about and working on, because they have attended the lectures, presentations, and poster sessions where scientists have discussed their activities.

The leadership experience is ongoing, and therefore leaders are continually adding to their knowledge. Their frequent presence in the field also sets an important example for employees, whose face-to-face encounters with customers and peers are critical to the further development of both their company and career. Merely telling employees to get out and expand their consciousness doesn't work anymore (if it ever did). Merely telling employees to do anything has gone the way of the buggy whip. Effective leadership means setting a good example. Employees pay closer attention to what leaders do than what they say. I suspect they always have.

Leaders need to trust their staffs and employees, not only to follow their example, but to think for themselves and make both ethically and strategically correct decisions. Leaders, obviously, must have the trust of their people if the organization is going to function effectively. But, in order to have that trust, leaders themselves must trust others. They must trust their officers and employees with all kinds of information and with the freedom and authority to make as many of their own decisions as possible.

Leaders are like coaches. They have confidence in their players to carry out their assignments once the players know what is expected of them. For that to happen, however, the coach first must communicate the game plan effectively. There can be no secrets or surprises. The successful leader, like the successful coach, makes sure that his or her team knows the overall objectives of the plan as well as the individual tasks of the play at hand.

Of course, a corporation is not a democracy. Leaders must make difficult, occasionally unpopular decisions in the best interest of the organization. Managers, preoccupied with control, tend to make these decisions either imperiously or defensively, hoping, if the decision is controversial, for the least amount of challenge and complaint. Leaders, trusting their employees with the facts, explain their decisions, which, even when disliked, are more readily understood and accepted.

Self-confidence, born of education and experience and nurtured by trust, is another requisite of effective leaders. Self-confidence enables the leader to build a strong team of officers and assistants, unafraid of potential rivals. It allows him or her to hear both the good and the bad about the organization and its leadership, understanding the necessity of the hard, unvarnished truth.

Self-confidence encourages the leader to look beyond the next quarter's results, to look at and plan for the myriad opportunities on the distant horizon.

We have had, at Medtronic, many effective leaders over the years, and never more than we have right now. By force of habit, however, we tend to label ourselves "managers." I think this is unfortunate, because, like many labels, it limits the way we envision and therefore perform our jobs. In this sense, we are talking about semantics. "Management," to my mind, is an out-of-date and narrowing term, one that connotes excessive control and, worse, manipulation. "Leadership," on the other hand, seems a fresher, more contemporary designation, suggesting imagination, openness, and growth.

I believe we ought to think of ourselves as leaders, and make no bones about the label. We need to think in leadership terms, always asking ourselves not merely, "How can we manage better?" but, "How can we be a more effective leader?" Our future may depend on the response.

NINE

Paradise

For most men and women who have devoted the lion's share of their lives to building and operating a company, retirement presents its own set of challenges. After 40 or so years in the saddle, not running a business can be as difficult a proposition as running one. Folks have compared retirement to a death in the family, the loss of an arm or a leg, or some other horrible condition that robs the individual of his or her sense of completeness and enthusiasm for life.

I can't say I haven't felt a twinge of nostalgia for the "good old days" – though, as we all know, the good old days were not necessarily so good at the time, and the past, as somebody once said, always looks better in retrospect. I can't say, either, that I haven't missed the day-to-day activity and camaraderie of a growing, evolving business. Thankfully, however, I've been able to maintain close touch with many of my Medtronic colleagues and collaborators. As I said earlier, my successors at company headquarters have always made me feel welcome and have encouraged my ongoing contact with employees, customers, and scientific partners around the world. I'm extremely grateful for that opportunity, and I would like to think that connection has been almost as good for the company as it has been for me.

I believe, though, that the real key to happiness and contentment after retirement is having developed compelling outside interests while we're still on the job. I'm speaking now of more than hobbies – more than golf or tennis or gardening, as engaging and satisfying as those activities might be. I'm speaking now of more, even, than my beloved ballroom dancing, which, to this day, invigorates and relaxes me like few other physical challenges in my experience. When I say compelling outside interests, I mean subjects and activities that challenge the intellect, encourage us to broaden our perception of the universe, and provide us with the means to act on our knowledge and experience for the benefit of humankind.

I was fortunate. I never had to search for such interests. I believe, in fact, I was born surrounded by them. Electricity and life together offered seemingly infinite paths for me to explore. I've been exploring those paths for as long as I can remember, beginning with the porcelain insulators and electrical outlets my uncle worried about, growing with my basement lab projects using the spare parts my mother salvaged from hardware-store junk bins, and continuing through my career helping develop leading-edge medical technology at Medtronic.

True, all of those paths eventually conjoined in my career. But other, not quite so visible or well-traveled paths have led off of the main ones. Those other paths – appearing at various stages in my life – have carried me to my other, albeit usually related, interests, and those interests have in turn absorbed most of my attention and energy since leaving Medtronic.

. . .

Sometimes what has interested me in retirement has been a very logical extension of what I'd been involved in at Medtronic and, indeed, has been an ongoing company-wide concern. Minnesota's unique amalgam of medical-technology companies and related organizations, dubbed Medical Alley, Inc., for instance, grew out of the interest of Medtronic and a handful of other manufacturers to develop and promote the area as a hotbed of medical innovation. I was especially interested in the idea, and became one of its early champions because I believed that technological progress depended on a collegial atmosphere and shared breakthroughs. Medtronic supports Medical Alley to this day, but, because most of the major issues now facing the company are national and global, not regional, in scope, the two organizations don't have quite as much in common as they once did.

In other cases, a retirement interest has been the somewhat unanticipated culmination of a project that was begun while I was at Medtronic. The Bakken Library & Museum is an obvious example. Like many (if not most) of the good things in my life, the library originated without a plan. Sometime during the middle

1960s, local Kiwanis clubs and other organizations began asking me to speak on the topic of cardiac pacing. The subject was new and unusual at that time, and because it held great promise for millions of sufferers of what was then a largely un- or under-treated condition, the therapy was generating a lot of publicity around the country. But I was an engineer and entrepreneur, not a theoretician or historian, and realized I knew little about the history of heart stimulation and treatment. Thus I asked an energetic young man named Dennis Stillings for help. Dennis, whose duties included the tending of our small but growing company archives, began researching the pacing phenomenon as it existed before Medtronic got into it during the 1950s. He quickly discovered the pioneering work of Mark Lidwell and Albert Hyman in the late 1920s and early '30s, and, from as far back as the 18th century, remarkable bits and pieces of medical lore, such as the resuscitation of an apparently deceased patient through the use of what might have been the world's first direct-current defibrillator.

I was fascinated by this information (as was Dennis and the audiences with whom I was sharing it), so we decided to expand the research. We would no longer be confined to matters of the heart, we decided, but would seek out data about the use of electricity throughout the long and varied history of medicine. Again we were surprised and delighted by what was out there. Searching through libraries and used-book stores, prowling around estate sales and flea markets, Stillings was soon coming back with dusty books, forgotten manuscripts, and all kinds of strange artifacts – evidence, most of it, of a preoccupation with electricity and health, electricity and life, that went all the way back to the ancient Romans, perhaps even further.

After several months of such discovery, Dennis's boss at the Medtronic library came to me and said she was going to have to let the young man go because all he seemed to be interested in was historical research. The woman had a point, of course, so I took Dennis into my cost center and began paying for some of the archaic materials myself. Freed to concentrate on his historical pursuits, Dennis quickly filled a room at the company's St. Anthony plant with old books and instruments, then occupied a full floor of an office complex in nearby Brooklyn Center.

By that time his quest for electro-medical material and machinery had gone worldwide. An old, forgotten device that had once been employed in the treatment of this or that condition might turn up in the basement of an English auction house or in the back room of a Mexican barbershop. One antiques collector Dennis discovered in London specialized in the unusual combination of banjos and medical devices! Among our important discoveries, we learned that if you asked an antiques dealer, for instance, about medical equipment, you would usually draw a blank. If, however, you inquired about "quack devices," you often hit pay dirt. In any event, it wasn't long before dealers around the globe were well aware of the kinds of things we were looking for.

Needless to say, it wasn't long, either, before we were once more running out of room. I decided, finally, to establish an independent nonprofit organization and obtain permanent space to ensure the proper care and development of the collection. In 1976, the organization purchased a large, handsome private home, built in 1930 on a lovely, semi-secluded wooded lot overlooking Lake Calhoun in south Minneapolis. We added a 20-by-60-foot climate-controlled underground vault to store the historical materials and books, and opened part of the house to scholars and the public.

Today the "little research project" that began with the acceptance of a request to speak to a Kiwanis Club is the world's finest collection devoted to the history of "electricity in life," numbering more than 11,000 rare books and 2,000 scientific and medical devices. With an annual budget of more than $1 million and a full-time staff of 12, "The Bakken," as it has become known throughout the world, is now the site of a broad range of scientific, educational, and cultural activities, including scholarly research, teacher-enrichment programs, student field trips, even chamber-music concerts. Currently, more than 4,500 schoolchildren a year take part in the field trips and tour the exhibits (a recent program highlighted the Frankenstein legend, while another celebrated Benjamin Franklin's birthday). A new mentoring program is helping young people develop their natural spirit of scientific inquiry through science projects on robots and other topics. Programs for adults include a series of innovative and informative *conversazioni*, featuring such leaders in modern pacing history as Walt Lillehei, Tom Holloran, and yours truly. I'm pleased to tell you that The Bakken, under the leadership of executive director David Rhees, has become a valued, multifaceted resource for the entire community. The facility is currently undergoing a $6-million reno-vation and expansion, with the addition of new classrooms, exhibit halls, vault space, and reading room, as well as an aquarium room for our electric fish. With the increased space and amenities, The Bakken should be an even more valuable resource for students, teachers, scholars, and the general public.

Talk about *Ready, fire, aim!* None of us expected any of this to happen – certainly not on such a scale. If we had, we might not have proceeded the way we did. We might very logically and responsibly have told ourselves: "Careful, too much cost, too much distraction – and who will ever use it?" And what a loss that would have been to us all.

In still other instances the absorbing interest has been more personal. One day in 1986, a small note in a radio-collector's mag-azine to which I subscribed happened to catch my attention. The note described the extensive collection of an amateur ham-radio operator by the name of Joe Pavek, who'd been picking up and restoring radios dating back to the 1920s. A traveling salesman by trade, Pavek had discovered the vintage sets, in various states of repair, in small towns, on farms, in sheriff's offices, and so forth, going back several decades. When I first heard about it, Pavek's col-lection was stored in the basement of a Minneapolis hardware store, where, according to the note in that magazine, it was soon to be sold off or thrown out.

Motivated by my own long-running love affair with radios, I contacted the Minnesota Broadcasters Association and suggested that we jointly save Joe Pavek's treasures. The association liked the idea, and together we rescued the collection, promising Joe that we would maintain it. Pavek has since passed away, but I'm happy to say that his radios continue to sing, snap, pop, and hum. Indeed, the Pavek Museum of Broadcasting, housed in its own small build-ing in St. Louis Park, another Minneapolis suburb, now comprises more than a thousand different radios, including early amateur and aircraft equipment, built before 1930.

The museum, which also houses a working amateur station, is open to the public, provides educational opportunities for young people and schools in conjunction with the Bakken Museum, and is the meeting place of several antique and amateur radio clubs.

Though I'm no longer the museum's chairman, I'm still honored to be a member of its board, and make a point to visit whenever I'm in town.

Then there are the odd opportunities afforded by a long career in a particular field of endeavor, when experience, expertise, and curiosity come together to create a unique and unforgettable adventure.

Such was my 1989 participation in an expedition to the Pacific Coast of Baja California with an international group of researchers whose mission was to record the electrocardiogram of a California gray whale. The objective was to learn more about the relationship between the size of a mammalian heart (in a whale that heart can be the size of a Volkswagen!) and the velocity at which electrical impulses activate certain sectors of the heart. Such information would not only apply to whales, but tell us more about the heart function of humans as well. And how do you administer an EKG to a creature measuring between 30 and 40 feet and weighing somewhere in the neighborhood of 30 tons? Very carefully – to borrow the punch line from an old joke. Actually, the gray whales we sought are both friendly and curious. The difficulty for our group proved to be attaching to the creatures' rough, parasite-infested hides the transmitter-bearing suction cups that would allow us to track electrical impulses from the heart. When the suction-cup plan failed, the group, using a harmless harpoon-like device, managed to insert the electrodes with a stout needle, which gave us at least an abbreviated EKG reading.

That first expedition to St. Ignacio's Bay off the Baja coast – where gray whales were once slaughtered wholesale by commercial whalers – was led by Professor Frits Meijler of The Netherlands. The expedition included a number of distinguished scientists, researchers, and dignitaries from Holland, Mexico, and the United States, including Prince Bernhard of The Netherlands. I'm proud to say that the Medtronic Bakken Research Center was one of its sponsors. And though the data results were small – we were more successful getting an EKG on a humpback whale on a similar expedition off the coast of Newfoundland two years later – I couldn't help but marvel at both the breathtaking reach of modern science and the extraordinary capability provided by contemporary technology.

I was also heartened by the reminder that all living things, great and small, are connected to one another, and that the lessons learned from one among us can be readily applied to another.

. . .

My fascination with the role of the mind in the healing process – a fascination sparked several years ago by an incipient awareness that there was more to the relationship between electricity and life than merely "flipping a switch" – led to my passionate involvement with the Archaeus Project [see Chapters 1 and 2].

The society, which I helped form and in which I remain an active member to this day, is concerned, simply put, with the correlation between what we think and how we feel. The idea of a correlation between mind and body is ancient, of course. In our lifetime, the concept was hugely popularized by the likes of Norman Vincent Peale, the New York-based Protestant minister whose message of the "power of positive thinking" reached millions of people through books, magazine articles, and radio and television broadcasts during the 1940s and '50s.

I hadn't given the idea any more than passing attention until I noticed, during the height of my Medtronic activities, that many high-tech products seemed to be significantly more effective when prescribed and administered by certain doctors and nurses. In particular, those professionals for whom devices and medications seemed to work best would create in their patients the conviction that the technology was indeed going to make them feel better. Now cardiac pacemakers generally produce very definite results; their effectiveness in the patient is easily and immediately measurable. Most everything else, from drugs to devices to procedures, usually requires more subjective evaluation – and, to my mind, seem to depend more heavily on physicians first believing in them and then being able to transfer that belief to the patient.

To me, the reality of the phenomenon became clearer and clearer – that so much of what we do in conventional Western, or allopathic, medicine depended on belief, or, more specifically, on turning on the healer within us.

This was not, to be sure, the conventional wisdom within our Western scientific and medical communities 20 or so years ago. The efficacy of a device or a drug depended on its own therapeutic "powers" (meaning the powers invested in it by its developers and manufacturers), not on the mind and/or spirit of its administrator and recipient. The effectiveness of that device or drug, moreover, could be proved only by double-blind studies and statistical significance. Anything not proved effective by such means must be a placebo. Among the scientists and doctors with whom I worked the notion of a linkage between mind, body, and spirit was a virtual conversation-killer. I would bring up the topic over dinner with a half-dozen physicians, for example, and five of them would get uneasy looks on their faces and try to find a way to change the subject. Many years ago I gave a speech to a group of about 700 physicians at a professional gathering in Cleveland. They assumed, of course, that I was going to speak to them about pacemakers. Instead, I shocked them by talking about how double-blind studies and statistical significance cause great harm in medicine and how many sound approaches to healing those techniques actually destroyed. About half the audience walked out before I was finished.

But I was not alone in that opinion. Even then, there were respectable members of the scientific and medical communities who were sharing such thoughts. As a matter of fact, after that otherwise disappointing Cleveland speech, several of the doctors came down to the podium and said they agreed with what I was suggesting. And, more often than not, the one physician who didn't try to scuttle the discussion at that typical dinner party I just mentioned would chime in with something like, "Oh, yes, and let me tell you about my experience with auras and dying patients!"

Back home in the Twin Cities, I began to get together with a group of other deeply concerned individuals who were thinking along the same lines. These folks included Otto Schmidt, head of the biophysics department at the University of Minnesota; Dr. Karen Olness, who was then practicing at the Children's Health Care Center in Minneapolis; and a handful of members of the Medtronic family who were intrigued by the idea of a holistic approach to health and healing. We began meeting informally at my home in Fridley. Dennis Stillings eventually joined us and began assembling a library of materials dealing with the role of the mind and spirit in both disease and health. Just as we discovered when we began probing the history of cardiac pacing, there was a great deal more than we ever expected.

Several like-minded friends and I founded the Archaeus Project, in 1982, to gather and publish information and to promote public discussion on the role of the consciousness in health and healing. Originally headquartered in the Twin Cities, the Project, under the directorship of Stillings, is now based in Waimea, on the Big Island of Hawaii. More important, several hundred doctors, scientists, policymakers, and other interested individuals subscribe to the Project's publications, including its "Time, Mind, and Medicine" series and *Healing Island* quarterly, and there are always healthy turnouts for our conferences. Archaeus is not alone, either. Many groups with similar interests exist around the world, exchanging ideas via a growing array of books, journals, conferences, and on-line bulletin boards. A holistic approach to medicine – incorporating multiple traditions, disciplines, and techniques, and acknowledging the healer that exists within each of us – is no longer on the fringe. It is increasingly part of medicine's operative language. The idea of "cyberphysiology" the group promotes does not, I want to once more make perfectly clear, mean a world without technology. It means, instead, the integration of high-tech with high-touch medicine in which – and this is the key – the focus is on the patient, not the theory, hardware, or procedure.

As the years have passed, it has been my good fortune to find a place where such ideas are not only compatible with local tradition but where the ideas could be translated into actual practice. Archaeus not only moved its headquarters to Hawaii, it has, in the most meaningful way, "set up shop" here and is an active part of the Five Mountain Project.

. . .

"Interest" is not quite strong enough to describe my attraction and attachment to the state of Hawaii. "Passion" is a more appropriate term in my case.

Though born and bred in Minnesota, I was never a big fan of its long, harsh winters. Though we didn't travel much as a family, I could imagine what an easy, carefree life might be lived on a South Sea island, where the sun shone warm and bright all year round and where the water was – well, always water. Stationed in Florida during my wartime military service, I learned first-hand what bright skies and tepid oceans were all about. I discovered that I did not miss the changing seasons that many Minnesotans love about the northland – that, indeed, I much preferred a year-round summer. I knew way back then, even as I returned to the Twin Cities to establish a home and start my career, that eventually I wanted to settle in the tropics.

My second wife, Doris, whom I married in 1982, was similarly inclined. Doris grew up in Hauge, North Dakota, where her father had been the postmaster. As a girl hanging around the post office, she would see the glossy travel magazines with inviting color photos of exotic tropical locations. Surrounded by cold and snow, she, too, dreamed of living in such a balmy spot one day.

When we vacationed, long before my retirement, Doris and I were lucky enough to have the chance to visit some of those tropical lands we had dreamed about. On those trips, but we not only enjoyed ourselves as travelers on a two-week holiday, we also looked over the site with an eye on possibly living there. Over the years we visited such far-flung locales as Bora Bora, Tahiti, Bali, and many of the islands in both the Caribbean and Mediterranean seas. Finally, we took a good look at Hawaii.

I had decided, years earlier, that our dream destination would be situated within 10 degrees of the equator. The Hawaiian Islands, as it happened, lay about 20 degrees off the earth's mid-line. But that turned out to be a quibble. What we eventually discovered, on the Big Island of Hawaii, was the paradise for which we'd been searching.

I spoke briefly, in Chapter Eight, about Kona Village, where we settled in to learn more about the land and its people. The resort, made up of more than a hundred thatched-roof huts overlooking the bay on the northwest coast of the Big Island, was a little piece of heaven. The resort itself was a model of informal charm and almost inimitable tranquility. Not only, as I said earlier, were there no rigid Do's and Don't's, there were, much to our delight, no telephones, televisions, or locks on the doors. The location itself was everything we had dreamed about – even more. We were quickly captivated by the spectacular natural beauty of the place and the genuine warmth and goodness of the people. The weather, need I say, was perfect.

One day Doris and I drove up the coast a few miles, stopped for lunch at the beautiful Mauna Lani Hotel, and noticed a new condominium project going up next door. We walked around the grounds and talked to the sales staff, and before the afternoon was over we'd decided to buy one of the condos. (This was not something we had planned. It was, rather, still another example of *Ready, fire, aim!*) In 1989, we began building our own home about 10 miles south of the Mauna Lani. Hawaii became our official residence in 1991.

Like most newcomers in a very different land, we struggled through a period of adjustment. Happily, that period was brief. But the Big Island is not like Oahu or Maui or some of the other parts of the Hawaiian islands more familiar and accommodating to visitors from the mainland. The Big Island is very remote – far removed from the busier, more populated areas of Honolulu and Oahu in cultural, social, and economic terms. It is, for one thing, sparsely populated: its 4,000 square miles (a somewhat larger land mass than Puerto Rico's) is home to only about 130,000 people. Among those people, there is no majority. Everybody, including the one-quarter of the population that is indigenous, belongs to a minority group: Chinese, Japanese, Filipino, Korean, and Portuguese (many of whom have been here for several generations), as well as aboriginal Hawaiian and countless combinations thereof. Surprisingly, at least to mainlanders, there is little animosity among the various ethnic groups. Hawaiians tend not to see themselves as individualistically as other Americans, as separate either from one another or from their environment. Hawaiians are generally more spiritual than other citizens. Indeed, their designation of Caucasian outsiders, *haoles*, means, literally, to be without spirit.

Thankfully, even *haoles* can attain the Hawaiian spirit. We no doubt have taken a few missteps, but overall I believe that Doris and I have done our best to fit into our Big Island community. When we decided to build our home, for instance, we asked Hawaiian blessings on the land. We also hosted a couple of luaus for the builders, their crews, and families, making it clear that the creation of our new home was a community project. When I later became president of the North Hawaii Community Hospital board, I made it clear that I would not be operating on my own or with only other white men and women, but that Hawaiians would necessarily be members of that decision-making group. I met with one of the respected Hawaiian elders – one of the tutus, or "grandmothers," you go to for knowledge and comfort – and told her how our hospital would be different from other hospitals, how it would incorporate many philosophies and techniques, including native Hawaiian. The tutu looked at me and beamed. "You must be Hawaiian!" she exclaimed. "What you're talking about is Hawaiian!" Perhaps at that moment – more than any other – I personally felt accepted in the community, as someone with spirit, as a Hawaiian.

I remember thinking: This is for real. I am finally living what I've been working toward through the Archaeus Project and other activities. I am finally feeling the combined power of the mind, spirit, and body. I am home.

. . .

Though I had officially "retired" to Hawaii (I paid taxes in Hawaii and held a Hawaiian driver's license, among other tangible proof of my new status), I had no desire or intention to simply lie around in a hammock and enjoy the gentle trade winds. I don't think I could have done that if I'd wanted to. I discovered, early on, that I was energized by a new kind of electricity – one that's somewhat more difficult to explain, but is no less real and powerful.

Where we're located in the northwest quadrant of the Big Island, we're at the center of a rough pentagon made up of five large volcanic mountains: four on the Big Island itself and one only 25 miles across the bay, on the island of Maui. In the morning, when I drive from our home to the hospital in Waimea, the sun is just coming up over Mauna Kea, the largest volcanic mountain, in total mass, in the world. No matter how many times you see it, the sight is breathtaking, the experience profound. You feel a presence – what the Hawaiians call *mauna*, meaning power or energy. That energy is in fact so powerful that some mornings I have to pull over to the side of the road and just let it fill me up. What I'm feeling, what is filling me up, is the immortal heartbeat of the land.

Not long after our arrival in Hawaii, I became involved in a statewide organization called Friends of the Future. The group, composed of far-sighted individuals from all sectors of society, seeks solutions to a range of statewide problems. I became chairman of the Health and Wellness Division, looking specifically at the 29,000 people who live in the northwest corner of the Big Island, who happen to be, statistically speaking, in the worst health in the entire state. For a variety of reasons, including a fatty diet, relatively depressed socio-economic conditions, and lack of easily accessible health care, our Hawaiian neighbors suffer from a disproportionate amount of diabetes, hypertension, heart failure, and stroke. Because the region was served by only a small clinic, persons suffering heart attacks or injuries in automobile accidents, for example, were subject to time-consuming transportation delays to Hilo or other parts of the island, sometimes with fatal results. The North Hawaii Community Hospital, which opened in the spring of 1996, was one much needed response.

But the hospital, as significant as it is, could be viewed as only a part of the response to the Big Island's problems. The Friends of the Future (headed by Kenny Brown, one of the state's most prominent citizens) and other interested groups have recognized that other health resources are necessary. Our people need to know the components of good nutrition and a healthy lifestyle. They have to have a meaningful and tangible incentive for staying healthy – an insurance system, for example, that encourages and rewards healthy living. They have to have education and employment opportunities that encourage and enable physical health while providing self-respect and peace of mind. They have to live and work in an environment free of pollution and degradation. Our goal, as I described it in some detail in Chapter Two, is to one day be home to a multifaceted health and wellness center that would draw patients from all over the world – a Healing Island in the beautiful Pacific.

Clearly, there's no shortage of challenges and opportunities for a retired fellow in Hawaii. Much of my time during the past several years was devoted to the planning, fund-raising, and opening of the new hospital. But there have been other, related activities, too: supporting the development of solar energy on the Big Island, through, among other initiatives, a solar-car-building program in the public schools; speaking on the subject of the heart and cardiovascular system to students and civic organizations; putting together a four-year biomedical-engineering scholarship in conjunction with Tulane University in New Orleans, which is given to Big Island students who will eventually put their skills to work back here at home; working closely with native movers and shakers like former U.S. Senator Spark Matsunaga to encourage new business and job opportunities for the local economy. I've even had the opportunity to help save the green sea turtles of Kiholo Bay and preserve some of the buildings and character of Waimea's historic Main Street.

Doris and I still have a few moments to ourselves, but not many. While we have our own ballroom in the new house, we can't seem to find much time to enjoy it. The truth is, I'm on the go at least as much as I've always been, even during the height of my business career.

Ironically, now that I've located my earthly paradise, I can't seem to stay put here. I seem forever in motion, flying back to Minnesota for meetings with new Medtronic employees and board meetings at the Bakken Museum or for visits with my kids and grandkids, to New York or Dallas or London for gatherings of a professional or industry group, to California or New York to take part in an Archaeus Project seminar.

But busy as I am, I can assure you of this. My spirit awaits my return to Hawaii.

TEN

Full Circle

All this exciting, entrepreneurial activity in Hawaii has given me, among other things, a wonderful sense of starting life anew. In my middle 70s, I feel reborn, alive with the spirit. Some days I feel the same thrill of adventure and discovery I felt when Palmer Hermundslie and I began to realize the potential of Medtronic – without the onerous financial worries inherent in those long-ago ventures.

Thankfully, with Doris's help, I've managed to stay reasonably healthy. Part of my current well-being is due, of course, to the moderate lifestyle inculcated in me by my conservative parents, a lifelong aversion to tobacco spawned by those youthful basement experiments with cigarette-smoking robots, and a positive, self-empowering attitude encouraged and enhanced by my Hawaiian experience. Since establishing a home here, I have taken up several new "habits" that have contributed significantly to the health of my mind, body, and spirit.

I give Doris most of the credit, because it was she, more than anyone, who encouraged me to investigate the benefits of so many of the wonderful attributes of a healthy Hawaiian life style. Every week, for example, I enjoy three three-and-a-half-hour sessions comprising vigorous exercise, cranial sacral, acupuncture, and massage that leave me feeling wonderfully restored – absolutely improved in every way. Doris herself has found relief from persistent lower-back problems at a local chiropractor after years of ineffective treatment by some of the best allopathic practitioners on the mainland. We both exercise regularly and benefit from the administration of various complementary therapies, from body washes and acupuncture to vitamins and herbs, as antidotes to the wears and cares of everyday life. The essential concept is the integration of mental, physical, and spiritual health. Which modality best promotes that concept is up to the individual. Doris and I don't claim that our particular regimen is right for everybody, but it sure has worked wonders for us.

A couple of years ago I reached the point at which I had to seek treatment for a serious cataract condition. The cataract had gotten so bad, in fact, my right eye was almost useless. When my Hawaiian friends learned of the situation, they assumed I would fly back to Minnesota to have the cataract removed – perhaps to the Mayo Clinic or some other eminent institution. But I went instead to a local ophthalmologist in a small rural hospital here in Hawaii. My neighbors took that, they told me, to be a sign of my commitment to the area and its people, and, of course, it was; I firmly believe that I have to walk the talk if my word is going to mean something in my adopted home. But, truth be told, it wasn't a sacrifice on my part. The ophthalmologist offered state-of-the-art technology, and he and his nurse gave me the kind of healing touch care that I desired. And, all things considered, I don't think I could have received better treatment anywhere.

I'm also – obviously, I suppose – a believer in the active life. Few retirees have sadder lives than those who have, or choose to have, nothing to do, nowhere to go, nothing more to learn or accomplish. I think good health depends in large part on a busy regimen that keeps us focused on the road ahead, on our fellow men and women, and on the community to which we all belong in this lifetime. Some people are surprised by my bulging agenda. "Why do you stay so active?" they ask me. "You're retired. You've earned a rest. Why not take it easy?" Well, the short answer is, I just can't seem to do otherwise. I was brought up believing that idle hands are the devil's workshop. More to the point, I was taught to believe that we have a responsibility to our fellow human beings, and I eventually developed a company whose mission was and is to help people live richer, fuller, healthier lives. Besides, I'm having fun. I feel good about what I'm doing, especially when I see that what I'm doing is making a difference in people's lives. Thus, alive and able, I remain on the go, energized by my Hawaiian experience, but also highly charged by the opportunity to both get and give wherever I go, including back in my original home town.

. . .

A few years ago, during one of my frequent visits to the Twin Cities, I was privileged to deliver the commencement address to my alma mater, the Institute of Technology at the University of Minnesota. Speaking to groups of students had become something I was doing fairly often at this new stage in my life, and I found it both a challenge and an honor, as well as yet another opportunity to share – to give back – some of what I'd learned over the years.

Reviewing that particular speech today, I believe it accurately and succinctly summed up not only the major reasons for the success I've enjoyed in business, but my personal "action plan" to this moment. Allow me to re-state, in abbreviated and edited form, some of those remarks right here.

My theme – no surprise – was *Ready, fire, aim!* I began by providing two examples of how the concept worked for us in the early days of Medtronic:

In 1949, I was in graduate school in electrical engineering. To be of service and because of my long-term interest, I spent some time repairing early medical electronic devices for the University of Minnesota and Abbott Northwestern Hospitals. *Ready.* There seemed to be a need, so one evening at a family gathering my brother-in-law and I decided to set up a company to service such equipment. *Fire.* We started Medtronic in a garage. We didn't analyze or study the market, we just did it. However, servicing was not as profitable as we liked, so we adjusted our *aim* and started selling other manufacturers' medical electronic equipment. Please note Medtronic was not created to manufacture pacemakers. That came eight years later as we continued to adjust our aim.

Selling and servicing other manufacturers' equipment, we became acquainted with the surgeons at the U of M – namely Dr. C. Walton Lillehei and his colleagues. In 1957, after a massive power blackout, one of the so-called "blue babies" Lillehei and his team were treating for heart block died when the big AC-powered pacemakers that were keeping the children alive following surgery failed. Because we were there, we had the opportunity to make the first wearable, battery-powered, transistorized pacemaker prototype. *Ready.*

It was just four weeks from the definition of need until those U of M doctors used the unit on children. *Fire.* The first unit was not child-proof, so we corrected our *aim* and so began our manufacture of pacemakers for individuals – first for infants, then for adults. Millions of patients have since been restored to full life with the help of implantable pacemakers.

The same philosophy of action has been Medtronic's mode of operation throughout its history. We do a great deal of careful planning, but we look for the unexpected chance to act quickly on those opportunities and also on problems. I could cite a long list of positive results – as well as some missed opportunities where we waited too long to fire.

The lesson is:

Have a bias for action!

Use your intuition!

Think out of the box!

Don't over-analyze!

Don't hesitate while looking for the perfect result!

Do it!

Correct your aim later.

So how do we get ready?

We get ready by setting a personal mission, which includes a set of values, a goal that helps humanity, and a meaningful role for your life.

We get ready by continued learning and education – by reading books and journals, attending seminars and lectures, learning from other languages and cultures, and studying our failures as well as our successes.

We get ready by continually feeding our minds with information. The half-life of an engineer's or physicist's education is very short today, about three years. Even though I'm retired, I still study and read extensively to be able to consult with my company and other organizations.

We also get ready by developing a belief in our intuition. We visualize results – and hold that vision until it's a reality. I have sometimes been called a "visionary." Really, I have only described what my intuition told me.

We get ready, finally, by thinking in unstructured ways. We think like Einstein, create like da Vinci, and invent like Edison. Humorize ideas. Twist, translate, and look for crazy solutions until an idea is born. Chase the impossible dream. The impossible is a great challenge, but often a great opportunity as well. My dreams have been fulfilled, but now I have new dreams.

And how do we fire?

We fire by acting on our vision and values. We take the first steps, even if the direction isn't clear. We do something, understanding that one person can make a difference. We take responsibility for what we do. We act like a leader. We walk the talk and set the way. We act on our intuition.

We don't wait or plan to do something in the future "when the time is right" because the years go by too fast. We stick our neck out, risk our jobs if necessary, become a maverick, a raging evangelist for our idea. We act outside the accepted ways of doing things. We understand that failure is closer to success than inaction. We proceed fearlessly into areas where no one has been. The world is changing. We get in front of the power curve.

And how do we aim?

We try again. Our first 10 attempts may not succeed, but the education we gain by trying is very important, and success will come with persistence. We flood our minds with information, read incessantly, examine the reasons we haven't succeeded, and fire again.

We don't drop an idea before it matures. Most good ideas will succeed given enough time. The target is probably moving. We need to assimilate all the information and continue to adjust the aim. We simultaneously aim at several targets in different categories. We become broadly knowledgeable, but remain focused. Different targets within the same focus can amplify each other. A corrected aim eventually brings in the envisioned success.

The world is rapidly changing. The years go by so fast. Don't hesitate! When in doubt believe in your intuition and envision your dream. Remember the three magic words: *Ready, fire, aim!*

The reaction to that speech was enthusiastic and encouraging. The hundreds of young engineers on the threshold of their careers seemed to understand and appreciate the lesson I was trying to impart. (I was also amused when, after the speech, one of the grads, a young Chinese man, wanted to talk to me about ballroom dancing!) One of the newly minted engineers took a brief detour on his way across the stage to receive his diploma, shook my hand, and told me he was starting "the next Medtronic" in two weeks. I told him I couldn't have been more pleased, and wished him all the luck in the world.

I knew, you see, that what I was telling those young people really worked. I knew from long, personal experience that the gospel I was preaching had a proven and practical application in real life. Though I had used the Medtronic story as my example (it was a Twin Cities audience, remember), I could just as easily and accurately have referred to our North Hawaii Community Hospital, where we had relied on our dreams, intuition, energy, and perseverance to make the institution a reality. *Ready, fire, aim!* It is indeed the lesson of a lifetime.

. . .

If I needed a reminder of that fact – if, for that matter, I required reinforcement of my lifelong objectives, or a reason to get up in the morning – all I'd have to do is recall one of our annual holiday programs at Medtronic. Because, to all intents and purposes, Medtronic's mission and my personal mission have been one and the same.

Medtronic's holiday program has been a company tradition since we created it in 1959 as a means of celebrating the fulfillment of our corporate mission to help people return to full life. The idea, in a nutshell, is to invite a diverse group of patients who have received a Medtronic device to tell our assembled employees how the employees' innovations have helped them overcome their illnesses and conditions. (Currently, four patients worldwide receive a Medtronic device every minute. In five years that number will double!) Over the years we have added several features to the program – the Medtronic choir sings, the Medtronic band plays, my old friend and long-time Medtronic employee Earl Hatten reads the Christmas story from the Bible, and a presentation from another religious faith is given – and, recently, have begun broadcasting the festivities to our far-flung installations via closed-circuit television. But the heart of the program continues to be the personal, heart-felt testimony of the patients, whose stories of suffering, disability, recovery, and hope leave not a dry eye in the house.

Last December's annual program included six patients: a Fort Worth, Texas, pediatric cardiologist who received a Medtronic.Kappa pacemaker to treat symptoms associated with sick sinus syndrome; a 13-year-old Los Angeles girl who received a Medtronic Jewel device to treat hypertrophic cardiomyopathy; an Excelsior, Minnesota, man whose doctors had relied on a Medtronic Octopus tissue stabilizer to immobilize a small area of his beating heart during two open-heart surgeries the previous year; a Belgian man who uses an implantable Itrel II neurostimulator to treat a tremor associated with Parkinson's disease; a Medtronic employee in India whose defective aortic heart valve had been replaced with a Medtronic Hall mechanical valve; and a semi-retired Baltimore, Maryland, dentist who received a Medtronic AneuRx endovascular graft to treat a life-threatening abdominal aortic aneurysm.

As host of the programs each year, I often wonder if the current edition's stories are going to be as gripping and poignant as the ones from the previous event. Well, I needn't worry; each year seems to outdo the one before it. Among 1997's highlights was the presence of Dr. Paul Gillette, an old friend of Medtronic's and one of the world's preeminent pediatric cardiologists, who was a patient at this presentation, not a presenter. We also welcomed the manager of the very plant that manufactured the mechanical valve that saved his life. The wife of the open-heart patient whose surgery was facilitated by our tissue stabilizer told the Medtronic audience, "God works through a lot of you."

Two of the presentations were especially affecting. Michel Placement, of Ciplet, Belgium, had suffered from Parkinson's disease for more than 20 years. His body was racked by tremors, and, recently, he was confined to a wheelchair, unable to stand, walk, or use his arms and hands without assistance, and no longer able to make a living as a bank official. It was as though, his physician said, he'd been "buried alive." Following the implantation of a Medtronic Activa® Parkinson's Control Therapy system two years earlier, however, Michel has recovered most basic functions – and then some. A short video presentation showed him all but totally immobile before the implantation, then, almost instantaneously upon activation of the neurostimulator, raising and waving his hands, rising from his chair, and walking easily across the room. Appearing in person at our program, he brought down the house when he performed a nifty pirouette en route to the podium. In his heavily accented English, he told the appreciative audience that, thanks to the device from Medtronic, he could drive a car, take a bath unassisted, and "even do a little dance if necessary."

Then there was Patty Folgar, the pretty California teen who received one of our implantable cardioverter defibrillators in 1995. Patty's story – told first by her physician, another old Medtronic friend, Dr. David Cannom, and then by the young lady herself – was almost unbelievable. Not only was Patty a victim of hypertrophic cardiomyopathy, two of her siblings had died of the condition before they had reached the age of 10, and both of her parents also suffered from enlarged hearts! Because her family couldn't pay for the implantable cardioverter defibrillator, Medtronic donated the device, and, according to Dr. Cannom, Patty's condition has steadily improved and she is living a normal, active, teenaged life, with the prospect of a productive adulthood. "Instead of standing on the sidelines," Patty told the rapt Medtronic assembly, "I can participate in any activity I want to." Thanks to her "wonderful little machine," as she referred to the implanted Jewel, "with high spirits I face each new day." I've heard a lot of patient tributes over the years, but, believe me, I had difficulty maintaining my composure during that one. So did most of the people in the room.

But then that's the point. The presence at the holiday program of those wonderful patients, from all around the world, is not merely intended to make us feel good at Christmas time. Their bright, smiling, pain-free faces and their bold words of hope and triumph remind us why we do what we do – why we are what we are – 365 days of the year. We are men and women who have dedicated our lives and careers to helping real people like Michel Placement and Patty Folgar overcome their pain and disability, and lead normal, happy, productive lives. It's the story of Medtronic, and it's the story of the Five Mountain Medical Community – and it's a story I never tire of either hearing or telling.

. . .

In my case, that story, recounted in this book, has been an adventure that's crossed both oceans and timelines. Looked at another way, the North Hawaii Community Hospital and Five Mountain Medical Community and other activities here on the Big Island may be viewed as simply a continuation of the journey I began back in Minneapolis all those many years ago.

It had its origins in those plainspoken, hard-working citizens of Columbia Heights, picked up momentum among the smart and dedicated scientists, technicians, doctors, and businessmen who made up Medtronic and its worldwide industry, and finally found its ultimate expression among the wise and warm people of Hawaii.

Thus, when people wonder what an electrical engineer from the Snow Belt is up to preaching spiritualism and holistic medicine in Hawaii, I have to laugh and say I'm doing pretty much what I've done all my life – only nowadays I don't have to wear a necktie! I'm a man with a mission, and the mission has brought me here, and I couldn't be more thankful for my good fortune. To have played a part in such wonderful developments, with such wonderful people, in such wonderful places, I can only describe as a gift from God.

My companion on this quest for the past nearly 20 years has been another gift, my loving wife Doris. It was Doris with whom I discovered this paradise, Doris who located the spot where we built our retirement home, and Doris who encouraged our new health-enhancing life style. Like Connie before her, and like my four beautiful and accomplished children, Doris has given me the grounding that has allowed me to do so much with my life. Her inspiration and support as I've moved into new areas of exploration and involvement has been unwavering. In fact, she has been an invaluable advisor and mentor, not to mention a tireless sounding board for my own ideas, giving me the confidence to go places I never dreamed I would go. I can never satisfactorily tell her and the rest of my wonderful family everything that they mean to me.

And wherever I turn in our new home I am constantly struck by the power, wisdom, and goodness of the local people who have welcomed us, given so freely of themselves, and taught us so much about the world we only thought we knew. Our Hawaiian friends know so much about so many things because, despite the distractions of modern life, they've remained closely connected to the natural forces around them. On November 28, 1997, Doris and I were honored to have Governor Benjamin Cayetano proclaim "Earl and Doris Bakken Day" in Hawaii, publicly acknowledging our contributions to the health and welfare on the islands. We were flattered, of course, but convinced, as always, that whatever we've given to Hawaii, we've been given so much more. We came here as students of the Hawaiian culture, and Hawaiians have taught us so much about their ways – and about ourselves. For all of our many and growing family of Hawaiian friends, I say thank you, too. *Mahalo a nui loa!*

I can't help but think of a couple of popular songs when I look back over my nearly 75 years on the planet. My life has been an impossible dream. I've lived it fully, and I've lived it my way. And, still, there's much more to do. Just here on the Big Island, I'm dedicated, as president of the Five Mountain Medical Community, to improving the health and wellness of all north Hawaiians. Thanks to the vision, commitment, and enterprise of the north Hawaiians themselves, we've accomplished a great deal already. Tutu's House is a valuable community resource of formal education and native wisdom, the purpose of which is to empower the individual to make wise and cost-effective decisions about his or her health. The NHCH is making history as a truly modern center for patient-centered, high-tech and high-touch medical care; recently, its high-level status was formally confirmed by the Joint Commission on Accreditation of Healthcare Organizations (JCAHO) – a major achievement, considering that many hospitals require several "tries" before being accredited by that prestigious industry-standards body. The Five Mountain project is breaking ground in bringing in patients from around the world, which will in turn lead to the creation of good jobs and meaningful careers for our Hawaiian neighbors.

As I write this, we're working hard to provide a broad-based education incentive for local students with a combination of career training, mentoring, and learning opportunities in such diverse yet related topics as culture, science, and religion. In addition, we're striving to educate both the public and the public's policymakers in the efficacy of Medical Savings Accounts as the soundest form of healing reimbursement, while promoting meaningful measurement of the community's Health Related Quality of Life.

As yet another wise man said, "Life is a journey, not a destination." So while, in one sense, it might be tempting to say I have finally arrived, in another I feel as though I've only just begun.

Afterword

By Susan Pueschel
Development Director, North Hawaii Community Hospital

I met Earl Bakken 10 years ago, after his arm had been twisted hard enough for him to declare "uncle" and agree to get involved with a dream called the North Hawaii Community Hospital. That initial meeting took place at the Kahilu Theater in Waimea, on the Big Island, where Earl was about to speak, for the very first time, to a small group of North Hawaiians. The title of his speech, "Crisis in Healthcare and Its Local Implications for the 21st Century," was enough to make me yawn, but as the one and only paid staff member of NHCH at the time, I was responsible for coordinating the event. It was the first public educational forum sponsored by NHCH – the local hospital that had been talked about for decades, but which, in reality, hadn't progressed much past the early stages of laryngitis.

It was 1988. Energy was starting to move around the idea – this dream, this urgent need. The NHCH was no longer just talk. People were indeed talking, but they were meeting and planning as well. Small rural communities in the area were discussing common concerns, and at the top of the list was a critical lack of timely access to acute hospital services. No longer was the northern section of the Big Island just a vast agricultural area consisting of sleepy isolated ranch and plantation villages, each with its own infirmary. The population was exploding, and its people had become, in essence, one big *ohana*. With the emergence of the hotel and resort industry during the 1970s and the slow, painful demise of the sugar plantations in the '80s and '90s, the districts of Hamakua, North Kohala, and South Kohala were changing. There seemed to be a new North Hawaii taking shape. Larger than the entire island of Oahu, this beautiful region of volcanoes and beaches was home to 29,000 residents and visitors who sorely needed a hospital.

And the movement began to swirl.

Recently, I learned about vortex phenomena. A vortex occurs naturally in various systems, from galaxies and DNA to human behavior and bathtub drains. When like-minded people share a dream or vision and work toward a common goal, an energy vortex-of-sorts happens. As it swirls, the vortex pulls like energy toward it, until a critical mass of energy begins to take form, often resulting in the manifestation of one of those miracles that skeptics say could never happen. Most people never experience a vortex, and if they do, it probably happens only once in their lifetime. Nonetheless, once a person has experienced a vortex, he or she wants nothing more than to experience another.

I'd say the NHCH vortex was on the delicate spin cycle when Earl took the stage that night in Waimea. It was an interesting speech after all. The speaker, a rather quiet, unassuming *haole*, or white man, "straight off the boat," as we say locally, was a famous inventor. It wasn't that I was not interested in global health-care impacts, either – it was just that I was too busy working to secure a new hospital for Waimea to be worried about the 21st century. I had to pick my battles, after all. Having worked locally as an emergency medical technician, where stabilize-and-transfer was the name of the game, I had seen far too many people not survive the two-hour ambulance transfer from north Hawaii to the nearest full-service hospital. So after Earl's presentation, while community members engaged him in casual conversation, it became apparent that a match made in heaven was about to take place. Not only did NHCH need Earl's vision, Earl's vision needed NHCH.

Over the next five years, the spin cycle shifted from delicate to heavy duty, and in 1994 construction began on what has since become known as "not just another hospital." During that time, Earl transformed himself from a pale *malahini* wanting only to relax in his little grass shack to the dynamic leader/teacher/mentor of the NHCH board of directors – and a local celebrity/philanthropist to boot. The NHCH vortex was on the permanent-press cycle, and a new phenomenon had occurred. Numerous other whirlwind projects had spun off the NHCH community initiative, with the genesis of a new YMCA and a hospice, among other developments. A beautiful community playground had been conceived, designed, and built by the minds and hands of the community's very own families. Everywhere I looked there was a North Hawaii this and a North Hawaii that. There had been no such thing as North Hawaii before NHCH coined the phrase.

And with NHCH well on its way, Earl did what Earl does best. He looked beyond the immediate urgent need for hospital services, toward the bigger picture of improved health, wellness, and quality of life for the people of his beloved Big Island home. Friends of the Future and Tutu's House were born. And from each of these vortices, smaller ones spun off. Then came Five Mountain Hawaii, yet another group of luminaries with a vision instilled and agitated by Earl. And there's no telling how many flurries *that* will create.

There are times when I envision Earl as a grand maestro, smiling contentedly from atop a high platform in the middle of a huge stadium, with hundreds of whirling dervishes spinning at his feet. And from the highest row, where I sit, the vivid colors and blends and gyrations are spectacular and dizzying, and then I humbly realize that I'm one of those orbiting people myself.

I've experienced the vortex in my lifetime, and I now know how truly blessed I am. Earl has experienced hundreds, and he's spinning faster than ever. I have had the incredible opportunity to work closely with Earl, to whirl all around him, to hear first-hand the stories of his life's works and his life's passions, and to witness his uncanny ability to see far beyond tomorrow. I have witnessed him inspire young and old with his vision. Yet Earl doesn't suffer from farsightedness. He sees the innate goodness within all people, and rarely do they prove him wrong. His wisdom, his generosity, his thoughtfulness, his heartfulness, and his humor (yes, his humor) have made me want to pinch myself at times just to make sure that knowing him in my lifetime isn't a dream. And yet it is. Dreams do come true after all.

Susan Pueschel

Medtronic Mission Statement

• To contribute to human welfare by application of biomedical engineering in the research, design, manufacture, and sale of instruments or appliances that alleviate pain, restore health, and extend life.

• To direct our growth in the areas of biomedical engineering where we display maximum strength and ability; to gather people and facilities that tend to augment these areas; to continuously build on these areas through education and knowledge assimilation; to avoid participation in areas where we cannot make unique and worthy contributions.

• To strive without reserve for the greatest possible reliability and quality in our products; to be the unsurpassed standard of comparison and to be recognized as a company of dedication, honesty, integrity, and service.

• To make a fair profit on current operations to meet our obligations, sustain our growth, and reach our goals.

• To recognize the personal worth of employees by providing an employment framework that allows personal satisfaction in work accomplished, security, advancement opportunity, and means to share in the company's success.

• To maintain good citizenship as a company.

Board, Memberships, Awards

President, board of directors, North Hawaii Community Hospital
President, Five Mountain Medical Community
Director emeritus, board of directors, Medtronic, Inc.
Chairman, board of directors, Archaeus Project
Chairman, board of directors, The Bakken Library & Museum
Vice chairman, board of directors, Pavek Museum of Broadcasting
Member emeritus, board of directors, Medical Alley, Inc.
Board of members, Children's Heart Fund
Honorary board of trustees, Science Museum of Minnesota

Fellow, Bakken Society
Fellow, Institute of Electrical and Electronic Engineers
Fellow, Instrument Society of America
Member, American Antiquarian Society
Member, Association for the Advancement of Medical Instrumentation
Associate Member, North American Society of Pacing and Electrophysiology,
    Inc. (NASPE)
Member, National Academy of Engineering
Honorary fellow, American College of Cardiology, 1991
Honorary fellow, International College of Surgeons, 1993
Minnesota Inventors Hall of Fame, 1995
American Heart Association, West Hawaii Division Hall of Fame, 1998

Special Award, Cardiostim 98 XX Anniversary for Engineers and
    Industry Founders, 1998
Association for the Advancement of Medical Instrumentation (AAMI)
    Foundation Laufman-Greatbatch Prize, 1998
Texas Heart Institute Innovator Award, 1998
American Heart Association, Hawaii, Heart Ball Honoree, 1996
1995 Minnesota High Technology Council Lifetime Achievement Award, 1996
American Creativity Association Lifetime Creative Achievement Award, 1996
Special Service Award, Richard Smart Big Island Community Achievement,
    Waimea, Hawaii, 1995
Honorary Doctor of Science Degree, Albany College of Pharmacy, 1995
IEEE Eli Lilly Award in Medical and Biological Engineering, Institute of
    Electrical and Electronics Engineers, 1994
Entrepreneur of the Year, Minnesota Entrepreneur's Club, 1993
Lifetime Achievement Award, Entrepreneur of the Year Institute, 1991
Officer in the Order of Orange-Nassau (royal decoration), The Netherlands,
    1989
Outstanding Minnesotan of the Year, Minnesota Broadcasters Association,
    1988
Honorary Doctor of Science Degree, University of Minnesota, 1988
Honorary Doctor of Science Degree, Tulane University, 1988
Achievement Award, Leadership in the Business Application of Science and
    Technology, Science Museum of Minnesota, 1988
Governor's Award for Medical Leadership, Minnesota Medical Alley
    Association, 1988
Centennial Medal, College of St. Thomas, 1986
NASPE's Distinguished Service Award, 1985
Centennial Medal, Institute of Electrical and Electronics Engineers, 1984
Engineering for Gold Award, National Society of Professional Engineers, 1984
    (honoring the cardiac pacemaker as one of the ten most outstanding
    engineering achievements of the last 50 years)
Med-Tech Outstanding Achievement Award, 1984
Outstanding Achievement Award, University of Minnesota, 1981
    (highest alumni award)

INDEX

A

Activa Parkinson's control therapy system, 143
Activitrax pacemaker system, 99, 103
Advanced Instruments, Inc., 42
Alcatel Company, 93
Allopathic medicine
    integration of chronobiology and cyberphysiology with, 26–27
    introduction of, at North Hawaii Community Hospital (NHCH), 7–10
Alternating-current pacemakers
    early cardiac surgery and, 47, 49–50
    photo of, 62
Andersen, Elmer L. (Governor), 67
AneuRx endovascular graft device, 143
Archaeus Project, 5–6, 12–13
    Bakken's involvement in, 129–131
    complementary medicine colloquium of, 17
    origins of cyberphysiologic health care and, 22
    2010 concept and, 23–24
Auwae, Papa Henry, 28

B

Bakken, Brad, 89
Bakken, Connie (Connie Olson), 38, 41–42, 58, 89, 100–102, 145
Bakken, Doris, 15–17, 78–79, 117, 132, 136–138, 145
Bakken, Earl
    army career of, 37–38, 57
    awards received by, 152
    ballroom dancing as hobby of, 101–102
    becomes CEO of Medtronic, 89–90, 100
    board memberships of, 151
    Centennial Medal from College of St. Thomas awarded to, 73
    development of leadership skills by, 100–101
    early business ventures of, 38–40
    early life and background, 29–36, 56, vii–viii
    education of, 32–33, 37
    family life of, 58, 89–90
    on future of Medtronic, 107–108
    George foreword on meeting with, iii–v
    health regimen of, 137–138
    hobbies of, 31–34
    honorary doctor science degree awarded by University of Minnesota, 73
    ideas of, viii–ix
    leadership philosophy of, 109–122
    life in Hawaii of, 132–134
    Medtronic formed by, 40–41
    photos of, 56–58, 68–75, 77–80
    post-retirement projects of, 131–136
    retirement as senior board chairman and company officer, 104
    at University of Minnesota, 38
Bakken, Florence (Florence Hendricks), 29–32, 55, 58, x
Bakken, Jeff, 89
Bakken, Lars, 30, 32